PSYCHOTHERAPY OF THE ADOLESCENT

PSYCHOTHERAPY

OF THE

ADOLESCENT

Edited by Benjamin Harris Balser, M.D.

INTERNATIONAL UNIVERSITIES PRESS, INC.

New York   *New York*

CONTENTS

5

INTRODUCTION

In May, 1955, at the meeting of the American Psychiatric Association in Atlantic City, a symposium on Psychotherapy of the Adolescent was held before the Section on Child Psychiatry. This symposium was organized so that psychotherapy of the adolescent could be presented from different levels. The program was as follows:

PSYCHOTHERAPY OF ADOLESCENTS AT THE LEVEL OF PRIVATE PRACTICE

Irene Josselyn, Institute for Psychoanalysis, Chicago, Ill.

PSYCHOTHERAPY OF ADOLESCENTS AT PRIVATE PRACTICE PLUS SCHOOL PRACTICE LEVEL

William Peltz, Institute of the Pennsylvania Hospital, Philadelphia, Penna.

PSYCHOTHERAPY OF ADOLESCENTS AT SCHOOL PLUS INPATIENT TREATMENT LEVEL

J. Franklin Robinson, Children's Service Center, Wilkes-Barre, Penna.

PSYCHOTHERAPY OF ADOLESCENTS AT CLINIC LEVEL

Sidney Berman, Children's Hospital, Washington, D.C.

PSYCHOTHERAPY OF ADOLESCENTS BY PEDIATRICIAN AND PSYCHIATRIST AT COMBINED CLINIC AND INPATIENT HOSPITAL LEVEL

Herbert I. Harris and Felix Heald, Children's Medical Center, Boston, Mass.

PSYCHOTHERAPY OF ADOLESCENTS AT INTENSIVE HOSPITAL TREATMENT LEVEL

Donald Greaves and Peter Regan, Payne Whitney Clinic, New York Hospital, N.Y.

DISCUSSION:
Exie Welsch, New York
Eleanor Steele, Philadelphia
Benjamin Balser, New York

Because of time limitation, the amount of material that could be presented had to be restricted by each individual on the program. However, for the purposes of this publication, each article was expanded so that the writers could freely and completely express their thoughts on the material that they were presenting. Subjects were assigned to the writers, and the manuscripts were sent in without any of the contributors knowing what the others had written. From this standpoint, it was gratifying to find unanimity of approach by all.

Supplementing these chapters are two additional chapters, the first of which is a psychotherapeutic interview with an adolescent, tape recorded, with accompanying interpretive commentary by Dr. Ruben R. Pottash of Philadelphia. It was felt that this detailed record would be of particular value in demonstrating the technique that was used, at least with this adolescent. The dynamics involved are interpreted in a running commentary along side of the actual material. The second supplemental chapter by Mr. C. Thurston Chase, Headmaster of the Eaglebrook School, Deerfield, Mass., focuses on the problems of the adolescent from the standpoint of the schoolmaster. This chapter was added to bring into our orientation the views of the school teacher, a layman, who has wide experience in the day-to-day reality adjustment of the adolescent.

In the usual text or reference book on child or adult psychiatry, there is an elaboration of diagnostic categories with therapy designed for each particular category. In the following chapters, it will be noted that diagnostic categories are rarely referred to. The psychiatric problems of adolescents are treated from the standpoint of intensity or degree of disturbance rather than nosologic difference. This is one of the striking characteristics of adolescent psychiatry. Diagnostic categorization is rarely employed in dealing with adolescents. This does not mean that treatment is always the same. On the contrary, as will be noted in the text, there are many approaches in the treatment of adolescents. These vary with the characterologic make-up of a patient as well as with the intensity of the emotional disturbance, and the methods used by that individual in dealing with the conflict and anxiety. It will be noted as one goes from chapter to chapter that this variety is maintained despite the intensity of treatment. It will be obvious on reading the text that therapy of adolescents differs from that of children or adults, yet contains elements of both. For example, psychoanalysis as a form of psychotherapy is frequently indicated in both children and adults, whereas in adolescents its full application is rarely indicated except in the late adolescent period.

The area of adolescent psychiatry has been something of a stepchild for many years. We have practiced child psychiatry with patients ranging in age from infancy to approximately thirteen years of age, and adult psychiatry with those from nineteen to twenty years on. However, until fairly recently, the in-between area has had little concentrated attention from dynamic psychiatry. As a matter of fact, there are very few medical schools that teach adolescent psychiatry to undergraduate medical students today. At some universities only a single lecture during the four years is devoted to this subject, while in most schools nothing at all is taught under this title. There are few reference sources on adolescent psychiatry and on psychotherapy of the adolescent. Some individual articles have been written, and there are a few books that deal, mostly on a superficial level, with some of the problems. It is hoped that this book will provide a reference source for psychotherapy of the adolescent.

For many years there has been a lack of facilities for

proper or adequate treatment of adolescents who require a combination of separation from the family and a protective environment. These facilities are appropriate for adolescents who work out conflicts and anxiety in a way which brings them into difficulties with either school authorities and/or legal authorities who represent society. One such institution available at the present moment which accepts adolescents is the Payne Whitney Clinic of the New York Hospital (see Chapter VI). There are others such as the Menninger Foundation, the Austen Riggs Center, and the Yale Psychiatric Institute, and the Wyoming Valley Children's Service Center.

There is another major need for private school settings to which children may be sent and receive schooling along with other disturbed adolescents and at the same time have available psychotherapy on as an intensive level as is necessary. The Wyoming Valley Children's Service Center (see Chapter III) offers housing for adolescents where they are supervised and attended by trained individuals, receive intensive psychotherapy, and at the same time attend the public schools in Wilkes-Barre, Pennsylvania. This is also true of the Menninger Foundation. There are some schools that are organized to accept and treat emotionally disturbed adolescents, such as the Brown Schools of Austin, Texas; the Grove School, Madison, Connecticut; and the Devereux School in Philadelphia. These schools do not have psychiatrists directly on the school staffs but have them available in the nearby communities or medical schools. Some of the larger boys' preparatory schools such as Andover, Exeter, and Lawrenceville have part-time psychiatrists who treat those youngsters who have emotional problems in a normal school setting. They are not set up primarily for those adolescents who are disturbed but rather are dealing with problems in their students as they arise in the normal cross-section of the population. There are other hospitals and schools that have programs for the treatment of disturbed adolescents, but their total number is not great and certainly not sufficient to care for the actual community needs.

We wish to thank Dr. Clarence B. Farrar, Editor of the *American Journal of Psychiatry*, who gave us permission to publish these papers separately as a group. The *American Journal of Psychiatry* has priority on all papers presented at the American Psychiatric Association. Likewise, we wish to thank Dr. Milton E. Kirkpatrick, Vice Chairman of the Section on Child Psychiatry, and Dr. Leonard H. Taboroff, Secretary of the Section on Child Psychiatry, of the American Psychiatric Association for their help and cooperation in the preparation of this program. Our thanks too to Dr. David A. Young, then Chairman of the Program Committee, for his help and guidance in the organization of this program.

B. H. B.

1

PSYCHOTHERAPY OF ADOLESCENTS
AT THE LEVEL OF PRIVATE PRACTICE

IRENE M. JOSSELYN, M.D.

INTRODUCTION

Psychiatric treatment of the young adolescent is perhaps the most challenging, the most frustrating, the most baffling, the most anxiety-arousing, and the most narcissistically gratifying experience a psychiatrist can have. Most patients, regardless of their age, offer one or more of these experiences to any therapist. Rarely is any patient, except an adolescent, all of these in one therapeutic hour. Characteristically, with those adolescents who, because of an awareness of their own needs, accept treatment, each hour presents a panorama picture of many of the problems inherent in any dynamically oriented therapy.

BASIC PROBLEMS OF THE ADOLESCENT

While our main purpose is a discussion of psychotherapy rather than of the psychological problems of adolescence, it would seem important to clarify the particular therapist's concept of the basis for the difficulties presented. In the author's opinion, the primary picture in normal, as well as disturbed adolescents is that of an overtaxed ego. The overtaxation is the result of the impact of the biological changes that are occurring. These changes bring about an intensification of internal urges which threaten to exceed the adap-

13

tive capacity of the ego. The intensification of the sexual urges or, if the term sexuality is used in a semantically more limited meaning, their awakening is the most obvious source of increased internal tension. Sexual urges are by no means the sole source of increased pressure for adaptation. There is also a greater urge to achieve independence through a self-determined outlet for aggressive drives. The adolescent, in order to gain this sense of independence and individuality, believes he must rebel against not only the control of his parents—a control that if accepted represents remaining dependent upon parent figures—but also against his own conscience. The latter is in many respects an infantile conscience poorly equipped to function in an adult world. While in many instances rebellion actually would not be necessary, since parental relationships and the conscience itself would respond to an evolving change, the adolescent feels an urgency for change and cannot always accept the slow pace that evolving modifications demand. This urgency is in part a result of the biological changes that are occurring. It is also rooted in the adolescent's fear of the changes. He is both overly eager to reach adulthood and is terrified at its prospects. He wants to jump off the cliff because he is afraid not only that the path is too steep to walk down but also that it will end in an unfathomable jungle.

Two other aspects contribute to his confusion. First of all, he is emotionally more reactive to stimuli that previously were assigned easily to a casual place in his daily experience. As a result, his own feelings confuse him. As one patient who was unusually sophisticated about psychiatric problems stated, "I'm an unfortunate manic-depressive. I gather most manic-depressives are manic for weeks then depressed for weeks. They have a chance to get used to each state. Sometimes I go through the cycle several times in a day. When I'm depressed everything is wrong. I think I'd commit suicide except I don't have even that much energy. I guess if I were a girl

I'd cry, but gee—even that would take more energy than I have. And all of a sudden I'm ready to do everything. I feel sore at one person and, even if he is twice my size, I'm ready to fight. I'm nuts about someone else, and I'm dying to prove how good I am; but Doc, do you suppose I'm a schizophrenic? Just now I feel as if I'm not talking about myself but about somebody I've watched." When the therapist asked a few minutes later about the results of the football game the day before, the schizoid, manic-depressive patient was tranformed into an eager seventeen-year-old boy who had just been chosen captain of the high school basketball team.

In addition to this emotional lability and sensitivity, the adolescent does not know who he is. Because his body has actually changed rapidly, it is an unfamiliar structure to him. It is not only the external body structure that is new; it responds differently both externally and internally. The internal changes result in new sensations, which, whether pleasant or unpleasant, stimulating or guilt-arousing, are still strange and, therefore, may be anxiety-producing or at least confusing.

In addition to these aspects characteristic of adolescence itself, the individual is also exposed to the impact of the unsolved problems of childhood. Probably every conflict of childhood of any moment has a resurgence in adolescence. A realignment of forces occurs in adolescence that results in a modification of the original solution found in childhood. If the former solution was adequate for childhood, the modification in adolescence probably occurs more smoothly. If the conflict was inadequately solved earlier, the inadequacy adds to the complexities of adolescence.

Psychologically, the adolescent thus has to become familiar with who he is and what he is striving to express, and then to adapt the person he is to the reality of the world and the demands of a more mature conscience, the latter still in a state of maturational change. Self-definition, self-integration and adaptation are functions of the ego. Because of the multiple pressures to which the adaptive potential of the ego is exposed, it is not surprising that at times the ego is overtaxed.

The other side of the picture, and a fact that is significant in evaluating why under these pressures the adaptation of the individual does not more often fail and a psychosis develop, is an equally biologically determined increased energy available for ego-determined adaptation. Thus the adolescent presents a problem of an individual upon whose ego-adaptive capacity great demands are being made but also an individual with an ego reserve greater than at any other time in life. At times the ego is exhausted and symptoms indicating this exhaustion occur. At other times the resiliency of the ego becomes manifest, and the psychologically gigantic problems of adolescence are handled with surprising adequacy. Consequently, both as a result of ego exhaustion and of the increased flexibility due to the greater ego potential, a type of ego defense may at one moment appear to be effective, only, in a brief interval, to prove ineffective and be abandoned for another. One of the important basic principles of therapy with the adolescent is that of recognizing whether the immediate, presenting picture is the result of ego exhaustion or of ego resiliency.

A THERAPEUTIC GOAL WITH ADOLESCENTS

Probably one reason there is so little in the current literature in regard to general concepts of therapy with adolescents is because of the self-consciousness of the therapist. So often the most successful therapeutic results with this age group either are attained inexplicably, by seemingly unorthodox therapy, or by means scarcely justifying the dignity inherent in the concept of psychotherapeutic methods; at other times they have been accomplished too easily to warrant credit to the therapist. In contrast, so often nothing has been achieved in those cases in which the therapist was most convinced that he understood the case and was using the right therapeutic approach. In the author's experience, practically every successfully treated case of an adolescent warrants the criticism from colleagues either that the case was not "analyzed," an attack against which a psychoanalyst has no answer, or that the so-called treatment was just an example of common-sense or relationship therapy, an attack against which no psychiatrist has a defense.

The following summary of aspects of treatment of the adolescent certainly warrants both criticisms. It should be borne in mind also that the material is oversimplified. Each example of methodology does not imply that the results attained or not attained were the outcome of consistent use of a particular method with a particular case. In many cases all and other approaches were used. It is the flexibility of methodology that is as important as the method itself. The versatility required in the therapist that will enable him to vary his response several times in an hour makes it extremely difficult to define in any orthodox way the therapeutic procedure. While it is essential for the therapist at least to understand the basic conflicts with which the adolescent is struggling, success or failure in therapy is dependent to a large extent upon the skill of the therapist in accurately gauging the strength, fatigue, and the potential resilience of the ego at the moment. While this is essential in any therapeutic procedure with a patient of any age, it is the rapid change in the ego state so characteristic of the adolescent of which the therapist must be aware. There are no tried and true criteria by which to evaluate the adolescent's ego state. It can be done only by the intuitive, empathetic response of the therapist.

ROLE OF CATHARSIS

In a therapeutic relationship with an adolescent patient, whether he is seen only for scheduled hours in the office or in the framework of the young person's daily living, the help provided by the therapist is frequently of a primarily cathartic nature. The adolescent wants and needs someone who will listen to him. As the adolescent projects his thoughts and ideas outward, the therapist functions as a sounding board, thus facilitating the differentiation of the unreality and the validity of the ideas expressed. Many times in a therapeutic hour the patient will propound ideas suggestive of a very unrealistic grasp of how things actually are. The therapist, torn between a wish to clarify the underlying implications of the patient's concept and a wish to reveal the "facts of life," remains silent, paralyzed by his confusion about his own therapeutic tools. He finds ultimately that he does not have to clarify the situation to any great extent. He finds also that he can wait to understand the dynamics behind the adolescent's ideas. The adolescent himself recognized the fallacy of his evaluation of reality, and the dynamic significance can be left veiled.

This type of therapy is often more effective with adolescents than with any other age group. Frequently, with an adult, an hour in which the patient freely expresses his ideas results in a lessening of tension but little change in the basic picture. He returns to his usual environment, to be exposed to the same tension-arousing situations, situations to which he responds in the same way, with the resultant increment in tension and a need for another hour of catharsis. More often the adolescent re-evaluates the situation as he listens to the echoes of his own ideas and the few comments the therapist has offered about them. He is different from the adult patient in the degree to which he can facilely change his evaluation of reality. The apparently neurotic components in his evaluation of reality are not as fixed as they are in an adult.

Jane, a very intelligent girl of sixteen, had been referred for therapy because of a provocative defiance of all school regulations. In the early hours of therapy, she primarily expounded her social philosophy based upon the belief that all men were created equal. Her primary *raison d'être* at the time was to arouse her fellow high school students against the regime in school that said not every student should be given college preparatory courses. By her ideals all students should have a college education because she ardently desired one for herself. After several hours in which the therapist had little opportunity to express an opinion, he was able to question whether people were equal by her definition, or whether the real point was not that they should have the right to equal opportunities to develop their own potentials. The therapist was even able to point out that there might be some way to utilize intelligence tests to enable the individual to have that opportunity. The therapist's comments appear to be unfortunate. The patient put an end to the hour by leaving precipitously with the parting remark, "I thought you would understand." The next treatment hour marked the turn in therapy. The patient had listened to the echo of her own words, had thought over the therapist's comments, and had decided she herself was unrealistic. From that point on she used the therapist primarily as a representative of reality with whom she could try out her intellectually stimulating, but emotionally charged ideas. Many of her ideas were keyed to her own personal conflicts, a fact she was rarely able to face. However, she was able to recognize that she feared she was not as adequate as her brother who had different areas of ability than she, and that her concept of all people being created equal was a technique for denying her fear of her own inequality in relation to her brother. There was considerable indication during treatment that the underlying conflicts lost their impact upon her actual adaptive patterns as she aired them in terms of political, economic, or moral philosophy. It is impossible to know how many of the conflicts reached some sort of adequate solution. The judgment can be only superficial. Her adult life has been one of sufficient gratification, so that in spite of a positive feeling for the therapist and certain alertness in regard to psychological problems, she has not sought further psychiatric help.

THE ROLE OF THE THERAPIST AS AN IDEAL

At times the therapist's role becomes one of offering a real or fantasy person with whom to identify. It would appear on casual consideration that the therapist would most likely find himself in this role when the adolescent has had an unsatisfactory relationship with the parent of the same sex. Actually, the therapist is usually less effective in this role if the young person's relationship with the parent of the same sex as the therapist has been predominately negative. In this case the patient strongly resists forming a relationship with a person of that sex. The therapist is more often cast in the role of an ideal either when the relationship with the parent of the same sex as the therapist has been predominately good but must be broken so that the patient can achieve adult status, or when, while relatively good in many areas the relationship fails to meet the specific needs of the adolescent.

Mary, a brilliant girl of nineteen, sought help because of her inability to utilize her natural endowment effectively. Her pattern of response had been a cyclic one for two years. For about a six-month period her work at school would be brilliant, but she would limit all social contacts to an intellectual companionship with boys and girls. Then her life would change rather dramatically. She would become involved with girls who were sexually promiscuous, and in a relationship with an intellectually inferior and unambitious boy. In this relationship with the boy, the primary interest was free sexual behavior in which there was no consideration of the future. She really knew nothing about the boy other than his sexual skill and interest.

A brief history gives salient points as to the underlying problem. Her father was an extremely attractive Don Juan who evaluated women only in terms of their sexual attractiveness. He had been overt in his seduction of his very appealing daughter and contemptuous of her intellectual interests. Her mother, on the other hand, was a basically intelligent woman who had failed completely as a sexual partner for the father. She tended to live vicariously through the intellectual achievements of her daughter. When faced with her daughter's sexual behavior, her attitude was that the sexual role was the only true one for a woman, and she hoped her daughter would succeed where she had failed.

As a result of previous therapy, Mary had a great deal of insight into the significance of this family constellation. When she proudly told of sleeping with a different boy every night for four weeks without knowing even the names of most of them, she recognized that her father was each man's prototype. This awareness only pressed her to greater activity and a greater need to recount her episodes to her father. When he suggested she have intercourse with him instead, she commented that he was too late. A few years before it would have been fun, now she wanted younger men. She also entertained her mother with her stories of success, and pointed out to her mother that she was finally more adequate than the latter. Such was the reward of "insight therapy."

Fortunately Mary was transferred to a woman therapist who was young, the mother of three children. Mary soon commented that she liked the therapist but didn't know why. Mary was at this point becoming interested in academic work again. One day she reported to the therapist that she looked up the therapist's background. She had found that she was not only a professional woman and married, but had three children! How, she wanted to know, could she do that? The hour was a noninsightful one. The therapist explained how she did it. Mary, in subsequent hours, formulated an integrative pattern. She could be a student, a sexual companion, a wife and mother. Subsequently she married a man of superior ability, continued her own academic career, and is now a wife, a mother, and a professional woman.

An identification with a therapist of the same sex is not the only possibility. If the therapist is a person of the opposite sex, he may serve as a yardstick by which to judge others of the opposite sex. This is particularly true when the adolescent is still seeking the outlines for the love object he is striving to find in his struggle toward heterosexuality.

John, a very sophisticated boy of fifteen, had from the time he was about ten years old, found that women attracted him. An aunt, eight years older than he, had used him as an escort to night clubs. By the time he was fourteen, he discovered he could successfully compete with many of the men at the night clubs for her attention or that of other unattached women present. He learned about intercourse from practical experience with his aunt. He was referred for psychiatric evaluation because of his "sexual precocity," but accepted treatment because of his recognition that he wasn't happy. The beginning of therapy with a woman therapist was stormy. The age of the therapist detracted from her appeal to him as a sexual object. Her failure to be seduced by him was confusing. Fortunately she was able to give him help in areas far removed from his sexual fantasies. She thereby became a benign, supporting mother to him. His hunger to be loved by a mother became dominant. Gradually the woman therapist became an ideal, a woman who gave emotionally even though not sexually. Ultimately he fused the sexually determined image of the aunt and the giving therapist into one and chose a love object who combined the aunt's sexual appeal with the therapist's emotional qualities. This was possible probably because he came to recognize that while the therapist was not sexual object to him, actually in her own life beyond the office, she was not an asexual person.

Both the identification with the therapist of the same sex, and the goal sought in exploration with individuals of the opposite sex, may be reached as a result of impersonal discussions with the therapist that appear to be therapeutic, but are definitely unorthodox as psychotherapy. Such discussions often resemble a parlor conversation more than an erudite therapeutic hour. There is a difference between such interviews and conversation, however. The therapist has some understanding of the underlying conflict of the adolescent and attempts to carry on his end of the conversation in the framework determined by that knowledge.

Tom, age fifteen, was discussing with a female therapist his resentment that women demanded and received, men gave and gave. From the dynamic evaluation of this boy's childhood, it was easy to surmise he feared the destructive impulses of women, hated their power, and experienced considerable masochistic satisfaction in a passive role. Any attempt to give him insight into this met with insurmountable resistance. A philosophical interchange about what women might seek in a relationship, and the distorted ways the desire might be expressed, led to a no more significant remark from Tom than "Gee, Mary is that way but I date Lois—guess I better date Mary for a while." Mary was much more capable of an embryonic heterosexual relationship than Lois was.

This role of ego ideal or ideal of a love object can be very frightening to the therapist. It appears to place him in a god-like position which he knows he cannot in actuality maintain. The therapist is of course not in this god-like role unless, in megalomaniac fashion, he assumes it. The patient is only investing him with characteristics which the patient is either seeking for himself or in a love object. Because the therapist does not assert his own personality but watches the characteristics with which the patient invests him, he becomes the embodiment of the patient's fantasy. The fantasy will be discarded if the relationship is wisely controlled, when the patient attains an integration closer to his own ego ideal, or finds a love object having the characteristics that he seeks. It is a dangerous role to play if a therapist, trapped by his own narcissistic needs, implies to the patient that this is what the therapist is in reality, and no one should be different or love someone different.

ROLE AS A PARENT FIGURE

Parents have many roles in the life of the adolescent. The therapist frequently has identical significance. Many times the therapist of an adolescent is placed in the role of a controlling parent figure in order to prevent the adolescent from carrying out an impulse that would prove disastrous. The therapist does not have the margin of safety in therapy with adolescents that he has in dealing with adults. With the latter, unless they are acting-out patients, it usually can be assumed that the superego of the adult will control behavior during the hours between therapeutic sessions. This cannot be assumed with adolescents. With those adult patients who do have a propensity for acting out, the therapist in many instances can effectively control the patient by indicating that the therapeutic goals of the patient and the therapist cannot be attained if the patient does not inhibit his acting-out behavior. The adolescent rarely makes as comparably great an investment in therapeutic goals. Furthermore, even if the acting out is not controlled, the adult patient has established certain defenses against the psychological impact of the consequences of acting out. Most adolescents do not have these defenses adequately established, so that acting out upon an impulse may result in external consequences or internal ones of guilt or shame that are too overwhelming for the ego.[1]

The necessity of attempting to curb impulsive behavior in the adolescent presents a serious problem for the therapist. Adamant prohibition of the anticipated act places the therapist in a position of being equated with the prohibiting parent. Since the adolescent in his behavior is often acting in rebellion against his parents, he may also rebel against the therapist. If, on the other hand, the therapist avoids any attempt at control of the adolescent's behavior, he may find himself in the position of being a corruptible parent who confuses the adolescent, as the latter seeks an ego ideal for himself. The therapist, under such circumstances, invites an

---

[1] The chronically acting-out adolescent may not be so burdened but probably also is rarely treatable except in a confined situation such as an institution.

acting out that the adolescent could not tolerate for himself unless the part of him that wishes to do so were reinforced by the therapist's support.

If there are therapeutic indications for curbing the impulsive behavior of the adolescent patient, it is probably most constructively and effectively done when the patient's relationship with the therapist is a positive one and when the therapist is seen as a benign, understanding, tolerant but consistent parent figure who recognizes the needs of the adolescent for freedom as well as limits.

Rose, a fifteen-year-old defiant, provocative adolescent, disarmed her therapist completely the first time when the latter indirectly indicated disapproval of an anticipated act on her part. A former boy friend who had retained a first priority position in her love life was driving through Rose's home town on a coast-to-coast auto trip. Rose, in reaction to his invitation to do so, had informed her mother that she was leaving on Friday night with him, to share the week end of his trip. She had saved enough money to fly back from the destination planned for Sunday, to be in school Monday morning. Rose came to her treatment hour in a hostile, defiant mood. Her mother had forbidden the trip. The only way the therapist could function, according to Rose, was to convince her mother she was not a prostitute, she wouldn't have sexual relations with the boy, and it was nobody's business what the neighbors said. The significant aspects of the interview were as follows:

Therapist: Such a trip would be fun. You haven't seen Jim for a long time. I wonder if he is all that you remember he was.

Rose: I'm sure he is. How better to find out than through taking this trip with him.

Therapist: I can see your point. The weather is so nice. It would be ideal to take a trip this week end.

Rose: That's my parents' idea. They want to substitute a week end at the summer cottage with them instead of with Jim. Baloney.

Therapist: Scenery plus Jim is quite different from scenery plus your parents.

Rose: And how.

Therapist: But you know, Rose, I sort of see your parents' point of view too. I've a lot of faith in your standards and your ability to live up to them, but you know your plan puts you to a very difficult test. I'm not sure you aren't asking more of yourself than you should.

Rose: Listen Doc. I can take care of myself.

Therapist: You know, I agree with you. There's another side to it. You are asking a lot of Jim, too. You say he's a nice person, and I tend to think you are probably right, but going off with him this way may make it sort of hard for him to believe you really expect him to live up to his ideals. Do you suppose he might misinterpret your acceptance of his invitation?

Rose: I don't think he would, but I can see he might be sort of confused. I can make that clear though.

Therapist: You know, Rose, the opinions of others are irritating at times, but if their opinions are bad, even if unwarranted, it can complicate our lives. People could misinterpret what you and Jim do, and that misinterpretation could sort of mix up your life during your school year.

Rose: I don't care.

Therapist: Remember, other people don't know you as well as you and I know you. They wouldn't necessarily be just unkind in their attitude, they just wouldn't know any better.

Rose: Yes, I see your point. You don't think I should do it then?

Therapist: I hate to say you shouldn't, but I can't help but feel that the consequences are too great a price to pay.

Rose: Gee, I'm dumb. Jim said if I didn't go with him he could spend the week end here. We could all go up to the summer cottage. You think my mother would agree?

Therapist: That's the answer. You and Jim could walk through the woods, go dancing, and have three square meals a day provided by your parents. I'll call your mother and suggest this to her.

Rose: Gee Doc, she'll listen to you. This'll be fun.

Therapist: Better bring me back some spring flowers, or I'll never again try to get your mother to help you out in your plans.

(Rose brought back some spring flowers.)

The approach to Rose succeeded because the therapist had not in the past prohibited minor, questionable behavior on Rose's part. The therapist had established a relationship with Rose based upon a respect for Rose's underlying strength and ability to think through a plan and because the therapist had been honest in presenting his own point of view to Rose without forcing her to accept that point of view.

Such situations do not always come to such a reassuring ending. When they do not, the therapist may have to take more definite steps. If the threatened behavior is chronic and seriously threatens either the future of the adolescent or the rights of others, the therapist may have to assume the unpleasant role of authority and arrange institutional placement for the individual.

INSIGHT THERAPY

The preceding examples of types of therapy with an adolescent would appear to imply that insight therapy involving the deeper levels of the conflict are not a part of therapy with this age group. This is by no means true. Insight therapy into deeply buried conflicts is usually considered the therapeutic tool of psychoanalysts to be achieved only by the use of the classical psychoanalytic techniques. With adolescents, under carefully evaluated circumstances,[2] surprisingly dra-

[2] Under what circumstances this insight is effectively given is difficult to define. In the author's experience, a retrospective evaluation suggests that the therapeutically effective remark often was made with spontaneity indicating it arose from the "therapeutic unconscious," without labored preformulation. This, however would be a dangerous criterion, since it could easily lead to impulsive interpretative therapy that would overwhelm the patient. Probably this type of episode in treatment is primarily an example

matic clinical indications of a realignment of unconscious forces can be observed, resulting from a casual interpretation of a comment or a response of the patient. It may bring manifest results that would be anticipated in an adult only after months of analysis.

Perhaps one of the most dramatic examples of this was seen by the author in a case of severe ulcerative colitis of two years' duration in which an interpretation of a dream brought about a dramatic change in the boy's pattern of behavior and an equally dramatic remission in his ulcerative colitis. The case can be briefly summarized.

Tony, a fourteen-year-old boy, was referred to therapy by an internist who had found that all current methods of medical management of ulcerative colitis failed. Tony had been kept alive by repeated transfusions. At the time of the first interview, he was a bony skeleton covered with yellow skin. His colorless ears stood out from his head like wings and appeared as transparent as the gossamer wings of a butterfly. Any feeble movement resulted in a dyspnea that suggested he was in a terminal condition, a suspicion confirmed by the internist. The latter believed that the patient's anemia and his general state of malnutrition were of such a degree that any intercurrent infection would prove fatal if the boy did not in the meantime literally bleed to death. Tony's mother spoke limited English so the anamnestic material was never complete. It was known that Tony was the youngest of five children and had always been a good boy. He had always done well in school until the onset of his illness and was now unhappy because he could not attend school. He was a good patient, never violating any order the physician gave. Tony, though he spoke English adequately, gave little more in an interview situation than the mother had. Undoubtedly this was in part related to his serious physical condition. More important probably was his background of nonverbal, repressed living. The therapist, in a desperate

---

of the point made earlier—that therapy for the adolescent is most effective in those cases in which the therapist intuitively responds to the ego state of the patient *at the moment* of the communication.

attempt to elicit some emotionally tinged material, finally
questioned him if, in view of his age and interest, he did not
at times wish to rebel again all the care and restrictions his
illness required. This he denied. When he was finally questioned as to whether he ever felt angry, he answered that he
did—at times toward his older brother. In succinct and
minimal terms, he described how his brother had period-
ically been angry at his mother's nagging and had quarreled
with her, finally escaping the home by joining the army.
Tony felt angry at his brother. It was not right for the
brother to be angry at his mother and to quarrel with her.
The therapist commented that young people often resented
parental interference, and the brother did not seem to be
such a bad person. The patient disagreed. The next hour,
unsolicited, the patient told of a dream. He was in the
kitchen of their home, facing a closet door. The door was
closed. The patient could hear a voice urging him to open
the door. He was afraid to obey because he knew that wild
animals were in the closet. If the door were opened, the
wild animals would escape. They would, if free, destroy both
him and the rest of the family. Finally the voice became so
insistent that he opened the door and awoke in terror before
he saw the animals.

The therapist connected the voice with the comment
about the brother's anger and the possibility that at times
he too might feel angry. To this the patient nodded. The
only further comment about the dream was to the effect that
the patient feared, if he released his feelings, he would
destroy the family and himself even though his brother's
behavior did not. Following this interview, there was a rapid
sequence of events. The patient, with permission from the
internist, went to a Y.M.C.A. where a program had been
arranged for him that would not tax his physical strength.
Within a couple of weeks, he confessed to the psychiatrist
that, unbeknownst to his family or the internist, he had
abandoned the Y program and was spending that time playing baseball on a vacant lot a few blocks from home. This
he was able to do because fortunately he had made the acquaintance of a group of boys who, sympathetic about his
physical condition, allowed him gradually to become a part
of the group, first playing catch, then batting the ball but

not running, and finally running the bases. It was when the
last step had been taken that he confessed to the therapist
that he had been playing baseball. For the first time in two
years he was free of intestinal bleeding. Therapy soon had to
be interrupted because the demands of school and of outside
activities allowed no time for therapy. In three months' time
the physical metamorphosis of the boy was striking. An indirect follow-up was possible five years later when his sister-
in-law sought help from the therapist for a severe anxiety
state. She reported that she came because Tony felt the
therapist had saved his life. She said that he was physically
well, socially active, and academically successful.

While Tony's case illustrates an unusually striking effect
of a relatively minor interpretation, the following case was
carried for a considerably longer period of time.

Alice, a girl of fifteen, came to the therapist because of
her mother's concern over her infatuation with a twenty-
two-year-old boy. When Alice was nine, the therapist had
attempted to work with her. At that time Alice had no
friends in her own age group, was rude to adults, demanded
her mother's constant attention, and incessantly complained
of being dissatisfied and unhappy. The mother, a youthfully,
attractive, but immature woman was obviously not so concerned about her daughter's unhappiness as about the narcissistic blow her daughter's problems were to her.

Treatment proved fruitless during that early period. When
it was resumed, Alice was very free in her expression of resentment toward her mother. Her mother had always criticized her for being overweight, gauche, and unable to attract
boys. She had lost weight, developed pleasant mannerisms,
and won a boy friend. Now her mother criticized her for
acting "too old." She expressed a great deal of admiration
for her mother's still youthful attractiveness and her easy
social ways, wondering whether she would ever attain her
mother's social skills. As she talked about her mother, a
facial tic, characterized by a twitching at the side of her
mouth that resulted in lifting one corner of her lips so that
her facial expression was one of sneering, became very
marked. This tic had been present since the original contact

but, according to the patient, was becoming progressively severe. The history of the tic was of particular interest. It cleared up after a discussion of the mother, in which the patient elucidated many aspects. It became apparent that the mother's early criticism of the girl had caused her to feel she could never be as adequate as her mother. On the other hand, the young girl felt the inadequacy of her mother as a parent figure. Later, at the time of the second period of therapy, she recognized that the mother, by a persistent adolescent type of seduction, had effectively kept the father from manifesting any interest in his daughter. The tic was an expression of unconscious contempt for the mother as well as a means of denying the girl's own sense of inadequacy.[3] This explanation of her problem came as a revelation to the girl. Her answer to it was that as a girl of fifteen, she was adequate. Her tic disappeared, to return briefly when her boy friend turned to another, an older girl, and her mother pointed out Alice's inadequacy in holding men. The arrival on the scene of a new boy friend proved sufficiently therapeutic for the tic to disappear.

The indication for this type of therapy with the adolescent is one of the most difficult to establish. Because of the ego state of the adolescent, material will frequently come out in an interview that is easily interpreted in terms of the underlying conflict. Because of the reactivation of the oedipal conflict during adolescence, oedipal material is particularly apparent. Developmentally earlier material will also frequently appear in only thinly disguised form. The question then arises as to whether this material is so close to the surface because the defenses are so weak, or whether it is close to the surface because the patient is ready to deal with it. Obviously each possibility may exist at different times with the same patient. The author tends to be conservative in approaching the obvious material that in an adult would be repressed, and to deal with it only in general terms, relating

[3] It was probably also an identification with the mother's contempt for the girl as well as a protection against her own (probably oedipal) strivings. These aspects were not interpreted to her.

it to the current situation rather than handling it in a more orthodox manner. Thus, if a girl presents thinly disguised fantasies of displacing her mother in her relationship to the father, often much can be gained for the patient's immediate adjustment by a discussion of the universality of this problem, and the resultant feeling that girl friends, for example, will desert the patient if she is interested in boys. An assumption that, because the dynamic significance of certain responses, dreams or behavior is clear to the therapist, it is safe to interpret it in terms of the transference and the infantile neurosis, has, in my experience, at times led to a disastrous disintegration of the patient's adaptive capacity. It has at other times led to a pseudo-therapeutic situation, in which the adolescent uses the insight given to justify acting out and progressive absorption in an erotized fantasy life that, once fostered by therapy, the patient is extremely reluctant to give up. In the case of Mary her response to the first therapist's clarification of her conflict demonstrates that possibility.

Even a modification of classical analytic techniques is rarely serviceable in the treatment of adolescents. Perhaps this conviction is based upon a question of semantics. If adolescence is considered as a developmental period during which the impact of biological changes is of such intensity that the adaptive capacity of the ego is overtaxed, it would appear that the individual is in a psychological state in which analysis is contraindicated, no matter what the patient's chronological age might be. It appears from the literature that the modification of analytic technique that has proved successful with adult psychotics would be equally effective with psychotic adolescents. Certain of those modifications are also noted in the treatment of less disturbed adolescents, as perhaps suggested by the preceding material. A person, who, if one uses chronological age as a criterion, comes within the standard age range of adolescence, may be analyzable. Those are the cases in which the personality has become structured in the form of a discernible neurosis. In such cases the symptoms vary no more than they do in older neurotics. The ego has found some way to crystallize the personality. As long as we recognize that freeing the individual from the chains of his neurosis will at the same time expose him to pressures from which his neurosis protected him, and as long as we utilize modifications of technique, those individuals can be treated by methods more closely allied to adult analysis. In this attempt, however, many of the techniques of the child analyst must be combined with those effective in adult analysis. More direct support in interpreting and tolerating reality is often indicated. A case in point is that of Harry who, when he entered treatment, was chronologically thirteen but physically mature beyond that age.

Harry had had a brief period of treatment two years before when he developed a severe deafness that proved to be of hysterical nature. It developed coincident with the pregnancy of an older sister and served the purpose of blocking his sexual curiosity. As soon as his deafness disappeared his mother withdrew him from treatment, explaining that while she was grateful that his hearing had returned, the therapist had converted him from an unusually nice child to a real boy and that was not right.

Harry returned with a severe compulsive neurosis. He had many rituals, of which the following are only a few. Before he drank out of a glass, he had to tap it three times. Before he left for school, he had to walk to the sidewalk three times, return to the house door, touch the door knob, and then return to the sidewalk. Certain articles of clothes had to be put off and put on again a certain number of times. His compulsions controlled his life and precluded participation in many activities. He returned to treatment with an eagerness for help rarely equalled in an adult patient. He persisted, in spite of every attempt on the part of his family to interrupt it. Because the family would not provide the money for carfare to come to the therapist's office, he earned it by taking on a paper route. He persisted in treatment until his symptoms disappeared. During the treatment which lasted for two years, the basis of his hostility toward members of the family became clear to him. His compulsions were related to his wish to destroy certain members of the family, and the belief that his masturbation (which was compulsive in nature) would, if indulged in a certain number of times, result in the death of family members, a different number of times in his own death, but in salvation for both himself and his family if he practiced it the correct number of times. A mental blocking for arithmetic cleared up as the unconscious meaning of certain numbers was clarified, and as the unconscious sexual symbolism in addition, subtraction, division, multiplication and fractions became apparent. Through dreams and associations his incestous desires for his mother, his fear of castration by her and by his father, and his retaliative anger became conscious to him. Much of the material obtained was stimulated first by the daily living situation, in school, and in his social group, and could be understood as a result of dreams and associations which clarified his early emotional experiences. In spite of this analytical type of reconstruction, the real insight the boy gained, and the therapeutic results achieved, certain analytically atypical characteristics of the therapy were present. The couch was never used because Harry became panicky when it was suggested. Perhaps this resistance could have been overcome, but it was, in the therapist's judgment, unwise to attempt to do so. In a face-to-face interview, Harry would step away at times from unconscious material. He would talk baseball. It seemed that he needed this facile return to reality when unconscious material became too frightening. Perhaps as a result of this, and because of the therapist's concern, a negative transference never became a part of therapy. Any attempt to interpret the negative transference aspects of a dream lead to a blank wall. Harry would comment that the therapist was wrong and go on to other subjects. Transference material was utilized interpretively when the response was to other persons in Harry's environment and not to the therapist. As far as could be determined, Harry's conscious attitude toward the therapist was that toward an understanding asexual mother, but at the same time the therapist represented an ideal which he sought in sexually acceptable girl friends. Only time will tell whether this semi-analysis proved to have lasting benefit or whether, under the pressure of adult living, the symptoms will return or others occur.

One of the particular difficulties in analyzing an adolescent, especially if the patient is in the early phase of adolescence, relates to the transference. The nature of the transference reaction has many of the characteristics of that observed in child analysis. Because the parents are part of the adolescent's day-to-day living, they are real and tend to interfere with the establishment of a true transference, except fleetingly. On the other hand, a transference response may develop that creates a difficult treatment situation. Because of its intensity in those cases and the inability of the ego to utilize insight into it, it ceases to be a therapeutic tool and becomes a liability in treatment. Under such circumstances the patient may withdraw into a fantasy life peopled only by himself and the therapist, or may act out provocatively in response to the therapist's unwillingness to make the transference response a reality. While this occurs also in certain adult analyses, the possibility of it is always more nearly at hand than it is in the typical adult analyses.

THE PARENTS AND THERAPY

The preceding material ignores the problems of the therapist's relationship to the adolescent patient's parents. Although to cover this subject would require a separate chapter, a few comments about this question are valid within the context of this article.

There are certain psychologically sophisticated parents who, irrespective of the child's age, will accept therapy for their child as a one-to-one relationship in which they have no part. In some instances the parental attitude is the result of a real respect for the validity and privacy of treatment. This attitude may be a two-edged sword, however. In such an attitude there may be pitfalls for the therapist unless the adolescent's problem is of such nature and his ego strength adequate, so that the reality aspects of the living situation can be ignored. Rarely is this true, except in the older adolescent who is gradually crystallizing a neurosis with which to handle his conflict, and unless he is prepared to care for himself as a socially, psychologically, and economically independent individual. Some contact with the parents is therefore often indicated, not to win the acceptance of therapy, but to make certain that goals are clearly understood. Contact may be minimal in time, even though significant in the evolution of treatment.

In some instances the parental attitude of overt respect for the privacy of therapy disguises a justification for them to transfer the burden of responsibility for the adolescent totally to the therapist. This apparently sudden emancipation of the parents from the adolescent can represent to the latter the final and convincing evidence of rejection by his parents. He may not be ready to tolerate such objectivity from parents who have already shown evidence of disinterest. Therapy then may become to him a dangerous pitfall to be avoided at any price of psychological discomfort.

In contrast, there are certain adolescents, particularly those in the later phase of the developmental process, who respond best to a therapeutic situation in which they are treated with the same respect for their maturity that an adult expects. They are willing and able to carry the burden of reality if they feel they can understand that reality. If the parents then share this concept of therapy and accept the therapist's unwillingness to work with them, treatment will be most effective. If anxious parents are not always equated with meddling parents and parents who remain remote from the situation until or unless the therapist appeals to them are not always seen as rejecting parents, if instead the parental attitude toward treatment is incorporated in the over-all evaluation of the case, the relationship between the adolescent, his parents, and the therapist will have greater likelihood of success.

Certain parents seek help for their adolescent son or daughter because of their own inability to evaluate behavior. Many times their concern is unwarranted, and the role of the therapist is to interpret the picture the normal adolescent presents. Probably a large percentage of parents who seek help in difficulties of this nature do so because of their own unconscious impulses and needs which they both hope and fear will be vicariously gratified by the behavior of their child. This possibility does not necessarily indicate that the child is doomed to gratify the parents in this way. The parents' over-all ego control may be adequate to prevent their unconsciously fostering undesirable behavior, especially if strengthened by a conscious understanding of the child's stage of development.

In contrast to this latter group, there are parents who foster in an adolescent behavior that will gratify their own repressed impulses. Johnson's and Szurek's writings on this role of the parents in the disturbed behavior of children of all age groups are easily validated in the study of many adolescents. The ideal therapeutic solution to this problem is undoubtedly the joint treatment of the parents and the adolescent. If the parents are untreatable or refuse treatment, the case does not become hopeless, unless the adolescent is so encased in his relationship with his parents that no one can break into the closed circle and establish a different relationship with him.

Aside from these two extremes of the parents' role in the therapy of the adolescent, many aspects of the parent-child-therapist relationship become apparent during therapy. Often the indicated therapy for the adolescent is a modification of the environmental pressures to which he is exposed. The neglect to enlist the parents' cooperation in this may lead to direct sabotage of the program or failure to carry it out because it is not understood. Furthermore, the young adolescent at least needs his parents or parent substitutes irrespective of the skill of a therapist in the therapeutic hour. The parents cannot, therefore, be ignored. The extent of the contact and the nature of it will depend upon the degree of emotional maturity of the adolescent, the nature of the problem, the extent to which the problem is internalized or to which it is a response to an external situation, and the degree to which the parents' neuroses creates the disturbed behavior in the adolescent. At times therapy with the adolescent fails because his parents do not have sufficient contact with the therapist to have faith in the therapy. The adolescent who is still financially and emotionally dependent upon the parent cannot always, even with the support of the therapist, maintain a treatment relationship if the parents oppose it. The nature of the therapist's relationship with a parent of an adolescent must thus be defined in the framework of the therapeutic approach and the therapeutic goals envisioned in the particular case.

CONCLUSIONS

In conclusion, therapy with the adolescent would appear to require the utilization of all known therapeutic techniques. These variations of technique apply not only to different patients, but also must be available in each therapeutic hour. Therapy of the adolescent must be as changeable as the adolescent himself.

The choice of the type of therapy should be based upon the answer to two questions: first, what therapeutic tool will, at this moment, strengthen the ego sufficiently so that the individual can deal more adequately with his internal turmoil and reality pressure; and secondly, what insight or experience will facilitate healthy integration of the multiple drives and pressures to which the patient is exposed?

2

PSYCHOTHERAPY OF ADOLESCENTS AT PRIVATE PRACTICE PLUS SCHOOL PRACTICE LEVEL

WILLIAM L. PELTZ, M.D.

When one considers the changes and conflicts of normal adolescence, it is not surprising that young people or their parents occasionally turn to counselors or to therapists for help with their problems. In addition to the marked physical and physiological changes which are going on during the adolescent years, there is restlessness, confusion, and impatience; lack of stability, fluctuating enthusiasms and intense infatuations; laziness, forgetfulness, and inconsistency. The need for aggressive self-assertion and the desire for independence are opposed by the ever-present dependency strivings and the desire for privileges, but without involving a sense of obligation and responsibility. The high ideals of one moment are followed by outrageous behavior the next. The feelings of isolation and of not being understood, plus the needs to conform and to be accepted, conflict with the dreams and fantasies which sometimes lend a schizoid coloring to the picture.

When, in addition to these manifestations, one considers the variety of problems which frequently arise during these same years, the reasons for the necessity of professional help become even more obvious. For example, there may be problems in connection with premature or retarded physical or physiological development; difficulties in adjusting to parents or teachers or other authority figures; difficulties in getting along with contemporaries, and scholastic difficulties. We find symptoms of anxiety, phobias or depression; symptoms or traits such as compulsion or speech disorders; introverted or even schizophrenic preoccupation and symptomatology. There may also be undesirable behavior such as temper tantrums, enuresis, lying, stealing, excessive quarreling and bullying, truancy, and abnormal or precocious sexual activity.

Such manifestations of adolescence and symptoms may lead to difficulties which become apparent not only at home and in the community, but also at school. In view of their closeness to boys and girls throughout the formative years of life, one might have thought that schools would long since have traced behavior problems to their roots in personality development. Actually, until very recently they have considered antisocial behavior merely as being censurable and deserving of punishment. Only in recent years have they been attempting to find the reasons for such behavior and to correct the difficulties. Mental hygiene projects have been started and guidance programs have been introduced into more and more school organizations. Such help is most apt to be needed at the times of transition from elementary to junior high school, from junior high to senior high, and from high school to college. Guidance work may be conducted by home room teachers, advisors or trained counselors, and may involve working with parents as well as with the students. The difference between guidance or counseling on the one hand and psychotherapy on the other is a hard one to define precisely. In general, however, it can be said that the former is more apt to be concerned with external situations or factors, dealing primarily with conscious material and usually lasting a short time; whereas psychotherapy deals with internal conflicts as well as conflicts with the external world, handles unconscious factors as well as conscious material, and is frequently of fairly long duration.

During recent years some schools and school systems have been turning to psychiatrists and psychologists for outside professional help. Some psychiatrists work with special schools for backward or mentally handicapped children, whereas others serve as consultants to schools for normal children, almost always on a part-time basis. No reliable figures are available as to what percentage of school children need or actually receive psychiatric help when facilities are available. In colleges and universities such students have been found to represent 10 to 15 per cent of the student body (25). It is probable that the percentages in schools are somewhat the same. When one considers that the school population of the United States is 41,553,000 it is apparent that a great need for psychiatric help with this age group exists.

The number of psychiatrists who are connected with schools has been gradually increasing during the last ten years, but is still woefully small—probably amounting to around a few hundred at the present time.

Dr. Gerald Pearson in his excellent book, *Psychoanalysis and the Education of the Child* (42), suggests that every school in the country should have on its staff a psychoanalyst specially trained in working with children. This would certainly be an ideal arrangement, but even Dr. Pearson recognizes that it will never be achieved. By way of example, it can be pointed out that in the City of Philadelphia alone there are 225 public schools.

The psychiatrist who serves as school consultant may function in various ways. For example, he may participate in training programs for teachers or guidance workers; he may talk at P.T.A. meetings; he may confer with the principal or other faculty members on such things as disciplinary action, changes in curriculum for certain students, or discuss emotional and personality factors and their importance in relation to adjustment. He may also be called upon to meet with the students for discussion groups on health, family life, and sex education; and he may be called upon to see students in consultation or therapy.

He must be considerably more than a good therapist with adults and children. For example, he should know something about the local school system and about the theory and practice of traditional and progressive education. In order to be helpful in suggesting the right type of school for a particular student, he should be familiar with public and private schools, with day schools and boarding schools, with coeducational schools and schools that are segregated for boys or for girls, and with the special schools such as military, vocational, and the schools for backward or problem children who need special help (47). He should be familiar with psychological tests employed by the school psychologist, and should know about problems in connection with learning and reading. In order to fulfill his role within a particular school, he should learn as much as possible about the teachers as well as about the general program and morale or spirit in the school. He should work closely with the school physician as well as with the principal. He should be familiar with local psychiatric clinics and social agency facilities in order to cope with special problems which are not within his field of work. If he is consultant for a boarding school, he should know of psychiatrists in as many other communities as possible because of the need to make referrals from time to time. Though there may be slight variations in the facilities available at different schools, he should have some awareness of which types of problems should receive psychiatric treatment and which can be handled satisfactorily by faculty counselors, by the school social worker, or by the psychologist.

Several cases follow which illustrate certain aspects of the work of the psychiatric consultant at a school.

Andy, aged seventeen, was a junior in a boy's boarding school. His referral was precipitated when he took some books from the room of another boy and denied it in spite of his obvious guilt. The housemaster conferred with the dean and referred the matter to the discipline committee. They decided that psychiatric referral was indicated in order to determine the basis of the problem and to see if help was needed. The school physician was notified and the psychiatrist was then called. Upon hearing the details of the case from the housemaster and the dean, he agreed that a consultation was indicated. After the dean conferred with the boy's parents, and they agreed, arrangements were made for Andy to be seen. He was a serious-minded, conscientious boy who was ambitious to succeed and to be first in the sports in which he competed. His school work was poor. He was inclined to worry about things and to have occasional spells of moodiness and outbursts of temper. He had tried to be "one of the boys," but did not have many real friends of his own age, either at school or at home. When food was sent to him from home, he resented the boys coming into his room while he was out and helping themselves. Unlike the other boys in the school, he kept his food and various articles locked up. When questioned about it and confronted with the evidence, he became obstinate and denied it.

Family history revealed that the father, who had done well at school, but had left college after two years, was ambitious and had become a successful business man. The mother worked for five years after the patient was born and led a social life in the evenings. Andy was brought up by a nurse during his earliest years, and had felt lonely and insecure. At the age of nine or ten he would come home and tell his parents he had been having a wonderful time playing games with other children when actually he had been standing on the side lines.

The lack of security in his early formative years appeared to determine his problems and conflicts and the defenses he developed. It was apparent that he desperately wanted to be successful, probably to please his successful parents, as well as himself. His defense against the unhappiness of not being accepted by his peers became a sour-grapes attitude of not caring about anyone else. His failure to succeed or to be first in sports led to frustration and resentment which could not be expressed outwardly and which, therefore, produced moodiness and feelings of depression.

There was considerable identification with his ambitious, successful father who had arranged that the boy should attend the same high-standard school to which he himself had gone. The father had urged this in spite of earlier recommendations, based on psychological testing. He knew that Andy was of only average intelligence and that a continued mediocre scholastic adjustment was to be expected, also that he might have considerable difficulty if he was sent away to a preparatory school. The reasons for Andy's drive to succeed and to conform as well as for his rebellion began to be apparent.

After seeing the boy initially, the psychiatrist conferred with the dean and the housemaster, advising that the boy remain in the school if it met with the approval of the authorities, and that further psychiatric visits were in order. It was suggested that appropriate steps be taken to control the annoying pilfering which apparently occurred in this particular dormitory. Meanwhile, psychological tests were requested in order to determine I.Q. and any factors in personality make-up which might be helpful in working with the boy. Copies of reports and of correspondence with the family were sent in duplicate to the school.

Andy was seen once or twice a month between February and June of his junior year in school. The interviews were face-to-face and consisted mostly of factual discussions of the patient's background and of his current life situations. The psychiatrist explored various aspects of the patient's feelings and reactions and in addition made occasional interpretations and suggestions. The mother was also seen on two occasions; it was impossible to meet the father.

In his senior year, Andy made a better adjustment. The consultant saw him only once that autumn, and during the rest of the year he kept in touch with his progress through the dean and housemaster. Andy was on one of the school teams and despite trouble with one subject in which he needed tutoring, he graduated and was accepted in college. It should be noted that an attempt was made to offer help through several channels. The boy was urged to express his feelings, to see why he was having his difficulties, and to know that people at school were anxious to help him; through suggesting a change in the school environment; and through being in touch with the parents.

It might be suggested that more prolonged or intensive psychiatric help would have been helpful, but the amount given took care of the immediate situation and that was all the family desired.

This case is cited in considerable detail in order to illustrate: (1) a type of problem for which a boy might be referred to the school psychiatrist, (2) the method of referral and the way the case was handled by the psychiatrist, (3) the fact that to discipline such a boy without finding out the reasons why he committed the act might be to do him considerable injustice.

As regards the method of referral, it is suggested that ideally, after the school has determined the problem situation to the best of its ability, the psychiatric consultant should confer with the principal, school counselor, home room teacher, housemaster, and the school physician to decide which steps should be taken, and especially whether psychiatric consultation is indicated. If it is, the school should get in touch with the parents and secure their permission before the psychiatrist sees the boy or girl. In one school (Phillips Exeter Academy) a boy who seeks help on his own will be seen by the psychiatrist in evaluation without permission from the family having been obtained. If therapy appears to be indicated, such permission will then be secured before proceeding. Frequently the consultant will interview one or preferably both parents at some time. After seeing the child, he may request psychological tests, encephalograms, or other special procedures. This preliminary investigation may require several sessions. Eventually, however, an opinion is reached, and a course of action decided upon both for the student and for the parents.

Sometimes it is decided that the situation can best be handled within the framework of the school without the student even being seen by the psychiatrist. For example, it may be recommended that the school counselor or home room teacher undertake counseling or that some environmental change within the school, such as a change in curriculum, take place, or that the parents be urged to have the child drop back a year or go to summer camp.

The case of Andy was also cited because stealing presents such a familiar and difficult problem to schools. It gives rise to suspicion and distrust and may lead to innocent students being blamed. It is important to find the offenders quickly because it can seriously disturb the school's morale. Formerly when the culprit was discovered, usually as a result of devious methods such as planting money, he was scolded, branded as a thief, expelled from school and returned to his humiliated and irate parents. Whatever his problem may have been to begin with, one can be sure that it was made worse by this "traditional" method of handling the situation.

Schools are becoming increasingly aware of the fact that stealing is the symptomatic expression of insecurity and emotional conflict and that it is an indication of the need for therapeutic help. Punishment without such help may merely make matters worse. Hope for a solution lies in helping the student discover the underlying sources of the difficulty, and helping to resolve them. For instance, if the roots are found to lie in deprivation of love and security and in the development of hostile feelings expressed inappropriately through stealing, an attempt is made to help the young person understand this mechanism which works largely on an unconscious repetitive basis. One tries to give him sympathetic understanding in an effort to develop a sense of security, and to modify constructively, to whatever degree is possible, the environment in which he is living. The latter may involve not only the school, but also, ideally, his parental and home situation.

It should be pointed out clearly that this effort along the lines of common sense and mental hygiene does not mean that disciplinary action should not be taken when it is appropriate. If a boy is failing scholastically or manifesting antisocial behavior, whatever the underlying reasons may be, he must not be excused from facing the realistic consequences or penalties. Seeing the school psychiatrist should not become an "out" for antisocial behavior. The psychiatrist should, rather, try to help the young person come to live realistically. That implies facing the consequences of one's behavior in a realistic way. This means that when the basic standards which exist in any school are not met, a student must be withdrawn from the school community; just as when people do not measure up to the basic standards of the social system in the larger community in which they live, they have to be removed from the community and placed in special institutions. When the student is withdrawn, however, an attempt is made to understand the reasons for his actions and to help him profit by the experience so that he may avoid similar difficulties in the future. The school has then done more than merely reprimand and expel him, thus washing its hands of the situation. He and his parents have been made aware of some of the underlying reasons for the difficulty and some constructive recommendations have been made.

Sometimes the question of whether a boy or girl should be asked to withdraw from school relates not to antisocial behavior such as we have been discussing, nor to scholastic failure, which is often also an indication of emotional difficulty and conflict, but to clear-cut symptoms of mental disturbance—or to a combination of these three types of difficulty. If a youngster is frankly psychotic or if a serious suicidal attempt has been made, the indication for withdrawal may be obvious to all concerned. So, too, if his symptoms are extremely distressing to himself or to others in the school environment, there may be no difficulty in reaching such a decision. If his mental symptoms are mild, however, the question of whether he should remain in the school is not always an easy matter to decide. In such instances the school may need help in reaching its decision. Frequently the school physician will have seen the child and it is he, along with the headmaster or dean, who requests the psychiatric consultation.

In the case of Bob, we see a boy in his senior year of boarding school who was found to have symptoms of mental illness, but who was able to finish out the year while at the same time receiving psychiatric help. In connection with this type of situation, it should be pointed out that it is as a general rule easier for a student to remain in school than it is for him to withdraw and then upon returning subsequently to have to make a new adjustment. Close cooperation between the school, the parents, and the psychiatrist was necessary in this case.

Bob was an eighteen-year-old senior, whose father had been killed during the war when Bob was twelve. He was referred because of his bizarre behavior. He seemed to be overly interested in airplanes and military affairs. He would occasionally make the zooming sounds of planes, and was tolerated by his schoolmates as being a "nice guy" but peculiar. He was doing poor work scholastically and was barely passing in spite of his considerable efforts. The incident which actually led to his referral was his handing to his housemaster a note phrased in punctilious military phraseology, requesting some jet planes for the protection of the school. He had represented himself as "commanding officer, far eastern theater." In addition, he complained of having had several episodes of feeling confused or "out of touch." He was said to be a dreamer and to live in a fantasy world.

When the psychiatrist was called, he suggested psychological tests, neurological examination, electroencephalogram and psychiatric evaluation, providing the mother approved. She agreed and after seeing the boy once, the psychiatrist saw her.

When seen in psychiatric interview, Bob was apparently a serious, precise, rigid, yet bright youngster who was troubled by being unable to do academic work he knew he was intellectually capable of doing. His speech was precise and clipped and he carried himself with a military poise. He aspired to go to the Air Force Academy.

The significant comments from the report on the psychological tests were as follows:

> This is a patient of superior intellectual resources who is at present unable to perform on the level of his given abilities. Inability to concentrate effectively, preoccupation with certain wish-fulfilling fantasies and some disturbances in the formal aspects of his thinking promote this inefficiency. The wish-fulfilling nature of the patient's fantasy has progressed to the point where it is at least autistic and may be well on the way to becoming a rather well-developed delusional system. Similarly, we find considerable affective lability in the patient; on a conscious level, the patient is generally unable to accept his emotions and considerable internalization may result. His fanciful flights seem to serve as compensatory mechanisms for a feeling of severe inadequacy and worthlessness. These feelings are intensified by strong superego drives to succeed and perform in a perfectionistic manner. At the same time, the patient feels himself called upon to replace the father in the family constellation. While there is considerable anxiety and inner turmoil, the patient is unwilling to acknowledge his difficulties, and maintains a somewhat idealized self-picture. Diagnostically, we are unable to make the differential between a severe adolescent turmoil and a nearly paranoid schizophrenia. More important, however, it is clear that the patient is extremely disturbed at present and that unless immediate therapeutic measures are taken, further breakdown in functioning will result.

The impression was that the boy was a schizoid individual with bizarre thinking and behavior, and with episodes of strange or unreal feelings. Regular visits to a psychiatrist seemed indicated; moreover, attempts were made to take off as much external pressure as possible within the framework of the school.

The boy's mother was seen and she was appraised of the findings. She accepted the recommendations and made arrangements for Bob to be treated psychiatrically in the nearby city, where they lived. Thus, after the evaluation interviews Bob was not treated by the school consultant. His progress was followed, however, throughout the year by the consultant who kept in touch with the dean and school physician.

Bob remained in the school through his senior year. He failed to pass two courses, but was tutored during the summer in order to receive his diploma after taking make-up exams in the fall. Continued and more intensive therapy than had been possible in the school setting was recommended for him.

Whereas it was felt that Bob could continue in the school in spite of the seriousness of his symptoms, it was decided after a period of several weeks of observation and therapy that the next patient, Charles, should withdraw from school. His symptoms and behavior caused considerable concern to the other boys and to the masters. Moreover, the school atmosphere appeared to be upsetting to him. Consequently, it was decided that it was in his best interest to leave the school. Until he had been seen several times the decision was not an easy one to reach. In spite of the apparent severity of Charles' illness, however, the results of therapy have been gratifying.

Charles, a sixteen-year-old junior in a boy's boarding school, was referred because, in spite of his superior intelligence, pleasant personality, athletic ability and positions of responsibility in the school, he was constantly doing things in or out of class which led to his being in trouble. It almost seemed as though he was masochistically asking to be punished. He had a talent for spoiling every possible chance of success. He broke rules in study hall and when reprimanded, was contrite and agreed not to repeat the things he had been doing, but would do the same things five minutes later in plain sight of the teacher. He failed to carry out his obligations on student committees and came to be called "Mr. Irresponsibility" by the other students. As examples of his poor judgment he slept out one night on the playing fields and then left his blankets there so that they were discovered. On another occasion he smoked in a place where smoking was forbidden and then came and told his housemaster about it. None of his misdemeanors were serious in themselves, but added together they became a matter of serious concern. At times he seemed extremely moody and depressed, and his grades had fallen markedly.

The situation was discussed with the psychiatrist, the housemaster, the dean and the school physician; it was agreed that the boy should be evaluated psychologically and psychiatrically. Therefore, the housemaster suggested the referral to the parents, and when they agreed the psychiatric consultant saw Charles, and later his parents.

It seemed that the father was a kindly but domineering and controlling individual who had high aspirations for Charles' scholastic achievements, social prestige and economic success because of his own frustrations and disappointments along these lines. The father had actually directed and coached the boy in one of his extracurricular activities far beyond the point which an ordinary father might. As Charles put it, "My father called every play." Consequently, by the time the boy was referred, he had completely lost interest in this activity. The mother went along with whatever the father suggested. Charles went away to boarding school at twelve, and at about that time began having episodes of depressions which would last a month or two.

Charles was in the midst of a state of adolescent rebellion. He was somewhat suspicious of people and stated that various injustices had been done to him. This paranoid tendency was apparent in the psychological tests, too, but it was believed that there was more evidence of cyclothymic than of definite schizoid personality make-up. It was felt that he was rebelling against his strong, directive father and had displaced his hostile feelings onto the school situation. His doubts and suspicions of people seemed to relate to his feelings that his father, and therefore other people, were taking advantage of him, and there was at least some basis in reality for this attitude both at home and at school. He would get into difficulty when he would test out people's attitudes toward himself. His hostility, instead of being expressed outwardly, was directed inward, with the result that he became depressed.

He was seen once a week by the psychiatrist and therapy was ego supportive, with a realistic setting of limits and of goals. He remained in the school for a number of weeks while being seen, but his behavior became increasingly unpredictable and eccentric, so that there were comments and complaints from many of his teachers and many of the boys as well. Most alarming was his beginning to grimace and to make explosive sounds. There appeared to be a definite schizoid coloring to the picture. Before the fall term was over it was agreed by the psychiatrist and the school that he should withdraw on medical grounds, with the possibility of returning the following autumn if his condition should warrant it. He accordingly went home and attended the local high school. He continued to be seen psychiatrically at weekly intervals thereafter, and his parents were seen occasionally, as well. He made a good adjustment both at home and at school. The direction and pressure from his father stopped as a result of suggestions from the psychiatrist. The boy was aided in expressing his rebellious, aggressive feelings toward his father and in recognizing their influence on his impulsive, asocial behavior. He came to understand his behavior at school as an outgrowth of his conflicts at home. He saw in the therapist a friendly, nondirective male figure with whom he could identify. Moreover, some of his dependency needs were satisfied in the treatment situation. He became better integrated and more stable and developed a good relationship with his parents. He was able to finish the year at a local day school without further erratic behavior. Moreover, he was no longer depressed and regained his interest in the activity in which he had excelled. He no longer felt directed or controlled. Charles wishes to continue at the day school rather than return to the boarding school. He also wants to continue in therapy during his senior year, but will probably be seen at less frequent intervals.

Quite naturally, not all cases that are referred for therapy turn out as satisfactorily as the last one did. For example, Don was referred by the headmaster of a junior high school because of scholastic difficulty, daydreaming, swearing in class, and breaking probation rules. He had threatened to run away from school and home. The mother and step-father said that this child had been a problem child all his life. Even in infancy and early childhood there had been difficulties in regard to eating, vomiting, tantrums, and mis-behavior of various sorts. The parents placed all the blame on the boy, claiming that he had had everything in his favor and that they had made every effort to help him. They also said that he was a liar, that he was spoiled and irresponsible, and that he had threatened them with violence.

Don presented a history which shed an altogether different light on the picture. The mother had been previously mar-ried and there had been constant quarreling and accusations of physical abuse by her husband. Don believed that his mother had gone around with other men. She met her second husband and lived with him before they were mar-ried. Don resented this and hated his stepfather, who had slapped him the second time they saw each other. Moreover, he resented the stepfather's insisting that he change his religion. Don said he would actually like to kill his step-father because he was so unreasonable and unfair. He him-self suggested as the only sensible solution that he be sent away to relatives or to a reformatory because he would never be able to get along at home.

The situation was discussed several times again with the mother and stepfather. They felt that strict discipline was the only thing that would help, and wanted the psychiatrist to scold Don and make him do the things they felt he should do. It was suggested to them that perhaps Don's troubles stemmed in some or even in large measure from home con-flicts, and that he might be helped if they, too, were to re-ceive some help. This they resented and did not accept. When they saw that the psychiatrist was not going to assume the role they wished him to, they stopped Don's visits. He was still having his problems at home and at school when last seen.

This case illustrates not only the difficulties which are presented when parents are uncooperative, but also the significant role that parents play in the child's personality development, and subsequent emotional conflicts and problems. It illustrates, too, just as did Charles' case, the need for modification of parental attitudes if the child is going to be helped. It becomes apparent, therefore, that help is indicated for the parents as well as the children. In clinics this is achieved by having social workers see the parents while the young person is in therapy. In private practice, however, parents of adolescents are apt to be seen in therapy less frequently. They are usually interviewed one or more times by the practicing psychiatrist who serves as school consultant, at the time of referral and initial evaluation. If he feels that psychotherapy is indicated for them as well as for the young person, and if he is going to take the young person on in therapy himself, he usually cannot and should not treat the parents because of the resistance in the adolescent which it would cause. Unlike in the psychiatric clinic, the school psychiatrist has no social worker associated with him who can see the parents. Accordingly, after one or two interviews with them he often recommends to them that they enter therapy with one of his colleagues. Sometimes he himself will treat the parents and have his colleague treat the child. This plan is suggested if it seems that the consultant's association with the school might lead to excessive resistance in a student. Sometimes joint interviews are held. These may involve the parents and the child, together with one or both therapists (or any combination of them, depending upon the particular situation and the needs which exist). In the cases under consideration, the school consultant usually used his assistant as the second psychiatrist, so that one of them would work with a boy and the other with the parents if the latter were available. It should be added, however, that if the assistant was treating a boy, the consultant met regularly each week with the assistant and went over the case with him. Moreover, the consultant usually would see the boy on his monthly visits to the school.

On the whole, most of the parents who have been interviewed by this writer have been at least reasonably cooperative. It is worth bearing in mind that it is difficult for parents to accept the idea of their child needing psychiatric help. Conscious and unconscious resistances, projection of the whole problem onto the adolescent, and practical considerations such as financial limitations and conflicts of work hours are apt to interfere. Whether or not there is justification for their feelings in reality, psychiatric referral signifies to them a certain amount of failure on their part and leads to feelings of guilt. Sometimes they feel they are being blamed for things which they do not consider to be their fault, and they often feel the stigma of psychiatry even more than their children do. It requires great courage, humility and adaptability in parents to accept psychiatric treatment for their child, to cooperate in therapy, and finally to change certain values and relationships which they have never questioned but always taken for granted. When one considers the matter from these points of view, it is actually remarkable that so many parents can cooperate even to the extent that they do.

It will be recalled that Bob and Don both came from broken homes, Bob's having been broken by the father's death and Don's by divorce. Any child would have had trouble growing up under the circumstances Don had to contend with. Usually, however, divorce and remarriage are handled in a far less unpleasant and unfortunate way. The next case is cited in order to illustrate the effects that divorce can sometimes have on a child, even when the parents have made every possible effort to handle the situation in as ideal a way as they are capable of.

Eddie was a likable, fifteen-year-old boy who was referred because of his extremely poor scholastic work in spite of a superior I.Q. and extra tutoring. He seemed unable to make himself work, and was frequently late and forgetful. His interest span in various school activities was limited. It was apparent from his attitude and behavior that he wanted to be the center of attention. The school had tried praise for his successes and punishment for his failures, but neither approach had achieved beneficial results. The housemaster and the dean, knowing that he came from a broken home, thought that there probably was a psychological basis for the problems and so requested psychiatric consultation.

Eddie was seen at regular intervals during the brief balance of that school year, with at least some evidence of improvement. In addition, the psychiatrist saw the parents and arranged psychological tests for Eddie.

History revealed that Eddie was an only child and that the parents had been divorced when he was four. Neither parent thought that he had been aware of any friction, or that he had been upset by the divorce. They continued to live near each other and made every effort to do what was best for him. He lived with his mother, but saw the father every week end and at least one evening a week for several years. The atmosphere was congenial between his parents, and the situation worked smoothly. Even after both parents remarried and had other children, the relationship continued to be a friendly one. The mother and her new family moved to another city and the boy divided his time between the two families during his vacations. He was said to like his stepbrothers and sisters and to be devoted to his stepparents.

His parents realized that something must be bothering him which was interfering with his making a satisfactory adjustment, scholastic and otherwise. They hoped that psychiatric evaluation would help uncover the seat of his difficulties and that therapy would help straighten him out.

In view of the ideal and rather unusual situation which has been described, the results of the psychological tests came as something of a surprise:

> He has adopted the attitude that the "world (actually his parents) owes him a living" and he is going to get what is coming to him by "hook or crook." He is resentful and envious of his half brothers and sisters and feels

that he is being deprived of much that is "rightfully" his. Furthermore, he is preoccupied with sadistic, destructive fantasies of violence, murder and revenge. . . . The patient confessed to carrying a switch blade knife which he uses "jokingly" to threaten "newcomers" to the school. He also states that he hates squirrels and kills them whenever he gets the opportunity. He apparently enjoys the reputation he has at school of being "cruel."

In the light of this behavior and his preoccupation on the TAT with killing either the father or mother or both, his failure to work up to or even near his potential level of ability may be interpreted as an "acting out" of hostility and anger toward his parents; a "get even" attitude for his "mistreatment." His generalized reaction to authority, in fact, seems to be one of resentment and anger. He seems to be adopting the "get by with as little effort as possible" and "get something for nothing" attitude.

Structurally the picture looks precarious. Although "internal" ego controls seems to be stable enough, "external" superego controls are shaky, and the potential for psychopathic-like acting out is present. I would venture to guess that it is only a certain *esprit de corps* at school that is keeping this boy from engaging in more openly defiant, antisocial behavior. The "relief valve" behavior of "joking" with his switch blade knife, killing squirrels and failing in his school work can be viewed in a similar way. The inner tension is apparent from his Rorschach responses, and at present he is relieving it via the above methods.

On the positive side the boy displays good ego controls, reality-oriented thinking and the capacity for good object relationships. When motivated he is able to function at a decidedly superior level of intellectual ability, showing signs of original creativity.

As I suggested above, I feel that the school is the main stabilizing force in the boy's present situation and if he should be forced to leave for one reason or another we might anticipate some rather serious consequences. Although I would not label the boy a "psychopath," he has all the potentialities of developing into a serious social problem. I strongly recommend supportive treatment with the objective of helping this young man attain a more balanced perspective of himself and his relationships with his family.

This case is cited as an example of the possible effects upon a youngster of a broken home, even when the parents have made every effort to handle the situation in a way which they hoped would not upset or adversely affect him.

A home that is broken psychologically by constant quarreling or unhappiness, or by death, separation or divorce, is always bound to have some effect upon the personality development of the children growing up in it. It is hard to imagine that the effect could be a positive or constructive one. On the other hand, the ill effects on children stemming from a separation or divorce may at times be less damaging than the ill effects from their living in a home where there is constant discord and quarreling. It has been aptly said that divorce always does damage to young children and that the effects of this are experienced in one way or another in later years. Unhappy or actually broken homes have accounted for over half of the students who are referred to the psychiatric consultants in some schools (27).

With the exception of their immediate families, probably no one has more influence on the personality development of young people than do their teachers. Moreover, the teachers, and especially housemasters or advisers in a boarding school, come to serve, either automatically or by design, not as therapists but as counselors to many of the students. Consequently, it is fitting that the school psychiatrist function not only as a consultant and therapist to the students who need help but also as a consultant to the faculty. This can become an equally important or even more important role in his service to the school. He may meet with individual teachers to advise them about students whom those teachers are seeing and trying to help, or he may conduct discussion sessions or lectures with groups of teachers. The latter should probably include, in layman's language, the stages and important factors in personality development and make-up, the motivation and interplay of emotional forces, the role of anxiety and the defense mechanisms which are usually used to control it. The forms of behavior and emotional difficulties which are commonly seen should be interpreted, and the proper role of the teacher or counselor in trying to be of help to boys or girls who are having difficulties of one sort or another should be defined. Perhaps the chief point for the faculty to realize and understand is that serious scholastic difficulty in a boy who has the capacity to do good work, and serious and persistent misconduct are practically always indications of emotional conflict requiring help.

On occasions, students come to the psychiatrist's office of their own volition. This has happened in the writer's experience on various occasions when students were anxious or depressed, when they were worried over sexual problems or a girl's pregnancy. Several of these youngsters did not want their parents to know that they were being seen psychiatrically. The treatment of minors without permission from their parents always presents problems, quite apart from the practical necessity to charge for the visits. It is usually wise to urge them to discuss the matter with their parents or to let the psychiatrist do so. If they still refuse, the only alternative generally is to make it clear that they can only be seen once or twice unless the parents are informed about their coming and unless the parents agree to the therapy.

When the school asks the consultant to see a student, the psychiatrist ordinarily discusses the case with the referring person at the school, or sends a report to him. The psychiatrist has a dual responsibility: one to the student and one to the school. Therefore, the question not infrequently arises as to what information he should discuss with the people at the school and what information he should withhold. Fortunately, there is almost never any reason or necessity to reveal intimate details or other confidential material to the school, nor does the school expect it. Its main concern is to be guided in its course of actions, at least to some extent, by the psychiatrist's suggestions or opinions and to see that the student receives the necessary professional help. Students usually feel reassured when this is explained to them, although occasionally such is not the case; and then it is best, as stated above, to have an assistant or colleague treat the student.

Patients are usually seen in therapy once or twice a week. Some patients may be seen only two or three times, whereas others may continue throughout the academic year. The average number of visits per student would be about six or eight. There is some tendency for those who do begin therapy not to continue with it. The reasons for this resistance are many: the adolescents desire their independence and, thus, revolt against authority and authority figures; they tend to act this out in the therapeutic situation; they believe narcissistically that they can solve their own problems. They also are reluctant to talk about their hostile and sexual thoughts or acts; and they mistrust adults who, they believe, will not understand them; and above all, they desire to conform with others in their own group, and believe that they will be regarded as different or queer if they go to a psychiatrist.

No one chapter in this book will probably contain all that there is to be said about psychotherapy of adolescents; and there will probably be a certain amount of overlapping because therapy in the office or the clinic or in connection with schools is much the same. There may even be some differences in points of view because of differences in training, experience, and theoretical orientation of the therapists who are writing the various chapters. At the risk of repeating what is being said elsewhere, a few thoughts about the psy-

chodynamics of adolescence and the theory and practice of
treating adolescents are offered.

In the first place, some of the conflicts which the adolescent experiences are internal ones, whereas others are conflicts between himself and significant people in his external
environment. For example, the adolescent's problems which
are related to his struggle for independence may stem from
an inner conflict between his dependency needs and his desires for independence, or, on the other hand, they may be
the result of his conflict with overprotective parents. Such
struggles and conflicts may be manifested in submissive compliance at home or in school in one student, and in rebellious
behavior in another.

It is important to recognize that the degree to which one
receives love and security in the early years of life determines
one's capacity to love and be loved and to adjust happily to
other people during later years. Such factors can play an important part in influencing the adolescent's ability to make
friends and get along with people or his tendency to be a
"lone wolf." There is a narcissistic quality to adolescent
friendship, which may be seen in the tendency to choose
friends like oneself; and this, in turn, is of some importance
in the problems of ego identity, homosexuality and the
formation of cliques or groups.

It is well to recognize the reasons why young people strive
for academic or athletic achievement in terms of their needs
for security and desires to "belong," and to recognize the
sources of their insecurity and anxiety in their earliest condi-
tioning experiences. So, too, it is well to understand the
adolescent's development of standards and value systems, and
the influences on these by the behavior of older and contemporary people with whom the adolescents come in contact. The inconsistencies, which to many people are so
puzzling, should be understood in terms of the conflicts
which are going on in the unconscious between powerful id

impulses that are seeking expression and growing, changing superego forces.

One should keep in mind that in adolescence oedipal strivings are revived and now interact with an ego that has acquired new capacities and dimensions, yet faces entirely new tasks. With the increase of pressure from instinctual drives, the ego uses various defense mechanisms which it has learned to use in the past, and to a much greater extent than ever before. Two of the mechanisms which are frequently used during adolescence are intellectualization and asceticism (18).

It is important not only to be accepting of and comforting about adolescent sexuality, but to recognize that the various forms of sexual activity during these years play an important part in the process of object-finding and in the development of a more mature sexuality. It is well to understand in this connection that the attainment of genital primacy and the completion of the process of finding nonincestuous love objects of the opposite sex are two of the most important functions of adolescence (51).

The school consultant should be aware of Kinsey's findings, especially in regard to the differences in sexual interests and activity between boys and girls, and as to the differences in sexual activity among young people of the three educational groups into which Kinsey divides his population (35, 36).

Psychotherapy in general may be repressive or expressive, or a combination of both. It may be manipulative, educational, or supportive; it may be what has been referred to as "relationship therapy"; or it may involve catharsis in some cases and the gaining of new and helpful insights in others (39).

Various writers have pointed out the need to make rapid contact with the adolescent who is entering therapy, and to have the first interview possess an atmosphere of certainty and ease (51, 1, 37). Therapy with the adolescent is more apt to involve manipulations in the environment than is the case with adults. For example, changes in curriculum or in the home situation are sometimes arranged, as has been pointed out in the cases which have been cited.

During the teen years, therapy often involves the giving of support and also, at times, the giving of information. Probably the most important aspect of psychotherapy with this age group, however, lies in the establishment of a wholesome, maturing relationship with the therapist, who assumes the role of the ideal parent.

Dr. Irene Josselyn has pointed out that adolescents can verbalize directly the meaning of their feelings, without knowing what to do with the insights they possess. She points out, too, that in view of this, a treatment technique is indicated which differs from the educational approach often used with children or from the interpretative approach aimed at giving insight which is often used with adults. The adolescent, she says, "needs to be protected from the external situations that excessively stimulate his internal drives . . . In addition, he needs help in redirecting his libidinal drive toward less anxiety-stimulating love-objects," and he also needs "the opportunity to sublimate his unacceptable primitive drives into socially acceptable, psychologically constructive paths. Insight therapy should be utilized only when such redirection is impossible . . . The aim of treatment," she continues, "should be primarily to protect the weakened ego in order to facilitate its convalescence. As the ego is strengthened, personality structuralization occurs . . . Once the structuralization does occur, however, the individual is then ready for deeper psychoanalytical therapy . . . In such treatment . . . the therapist needs to be extremely sensitive to the ego's tolerance for insight . . . Psychoanalysis, even in modified form, is indicated . . . only toward the end of the adolescent period" (32).

The young adolescent is in an in-between phase. He is too mature for the techniques of play therapy, but hardly ever ready for ordinary adult therapy on the level of verbal communication. Therefore, at times, it may be wise for the therapist to make certain modifications in his technique and to maintain a considerable degree of flexibility. He may, for example, play checkers or darts with the young adolescent, or utilize drawing or painting as a way of establishing and maintaining the all-important relationship. He may explore what the patient would wish for if any three or four wishes, however fantastic, could be granted. Or he may have the patient draw a diagram of the interior of his home and discuss all sorts of details about living arrangements and household activities in terms of the diagram, partly with the idea of obtaining information, partly with the idea of facilitating the patient's ability to verbalize and overcome reticence and resistance, and partly to establish rapport (3).

The interviews are apt to have a conversational quality, but the therapist should be alert to the deeper reasons as to why particular things are being discussed at particular times. This does not mean that he should always make interpretations about unconscious motivations, conflicts and defenses. Actually, he should use caution and restraint about doing so most of the time. Perhaps weeks later, when the patient is ready for them and can utilize them, such interpretations might be made.

The therapist should be sincerely interested, accepting and permissive. The therapist should interfere or prohibit only in unusual situations when necessity dictates it, for instance, when a young person is about to act in a way which jeopardizes his or her future happiness. In less serious situations he might help the patient gain a better sense of reality through acting as a sounding board or through exploring the consequences of various courses of action. Often, especially when the consequences are not too serious, the maturing process may be more enhanced by permitting the adolescent to make an occasional mistake and thereby learn through his own experience rather than by hearing the advice or experiences of someone else. The young person is probably "sick to death" of hearing good and bad advice at home.

Various advantages of treating adolescents in groups have been described by Slavson (50), Schulman (49), and others. These authors pointed out that one therapist can be of help at the same time to a larger number of youngsters. Still greater advantages, however, can be seen in the stimulation of identification processes which occur not only with the leader but also in the peer group as well as in the element of support which occurs when others are present who are in more or less the same situation. It is quite possible that group therapy may increasingly be used in the years to come. Such group programs are probably more feasible, however, in clinics than they are in private practice.

In conclusion, it should be mentioned that what might be considered to be neurotic manifestations in adults appear temporarily in many adolescents as normal and natural phenomena which usually subside spontaneously. When they lead the young person to seek help, they often are relieved by a few sessions which are focused on the current situation. As a result of the conflicts leading to these pseudo-neurotic manifestations, adolescence is often not the happy, carefree time of life it is commonly and nostalgically considered to be. Recently a thirteen-year-old who had withdrawn from his friends was asked by his grandmother why he was not out having fun with them. "Oh," he replied, "there's nothing in life to look forward to any more; the best years of my life are over." Such episodes may seem somewhat amusing to those who realize that the "tragedies" of adolescence are of brief duration, but to the young person they are anything but

amusing. Those fleeting "years with pleasure rife, the short-
est, gladdest years of life"[1] which glide so swiftly by are in
reality often filled with turmoil, frustration and despair. It
is fortunate indeed that for the large majority of young
people, the best years of their lives lie ahead.

---

[1] Yale College Song: "Bright College Years."

3

PSYCHOTHERAPY OF ADOLESCENTS AT SCHOOL PLUS INPATIENT TREATMENT LEVEL

Indicating the Interrelation of Work with Patient and Parents

J . FRANKLIN ROBINSON, M.D.

Resident psychiatric treatment as practiced at the Children's Service Center is a way of making psychotherapy available for a child or adolescent. Work is undertaken at the request of the parents or the foster agency which is responsible for him. While the adolescent lives in residence for a considerable period (usually about a year), domestic responsibility for him is not surrendered. The parents or foster caseworker will maintain an active association with him and with the Center and have an important influence in his use of treatment.

At the Center, the adolescent is called upon to enter into an active group living arrangement in which the central interest is his use of individual psychotherapy. He attends the public school. He attends church services or Sabbath school. He forms friendships and participates in community recreational activities as he is able (Scouts, Y, teen-age canteen, etc.). There are two comfortable residences, adjacent to the professional office building, located in a residential section of town.

The parents of the patient, or his foster caseworker, will visit at regular intervals. On visits to Wilkes-Barre, parents usually remain overnight. They spend some time in and about the residence and also arrange to have time with the adolescent away from the Center (dining out, shopping, or on excursions—frequently the adolescent is with them overnight at their hotel or one of the nearby resorts). During visits parents have scheduled interviews with the child's therapist or a social caseworker. (Foster caseworkers have scheduled interviews with the child's therapist.)

The principles that have been developed in outpatient child guidance clinics are in good part applicable in residence. The application or request for service is considered with those persons who are domestically responsible for the patient. These will usually be the parents. Believing that an adolescent needs the continuing security of a lasting domestic association, we do not pursue applications with authorities who have assumed only temporary custody for the patient. We require that an agency which undertakes to provide psychiatric treatment for a child in residence be one which is equipped to continue to plan and care for him beyond the active treatment period. We accordingly consider adolescents for acceptance into residence for treatment who are under the custody of their parents or a responsible foster care agency.

Resident treatment is expensive, demanding of time and interest, and takes the child out of the home. The circumstances which bring parents to a decision to use residence rather than an outpatient service influence the manner in which work can be arranged.

Where the difficulty has been long-standing, parents become discouraged and are doubtful of the child's ultimate capacity to respond. They have usually failed in efforts to use outpatient services. They may feel increasing guilt about their part in the development and continuance of the difficulty. Some have believed from the beginning that the trouble was essentially within the child.

The intensity of the struggle or feelings of antagonism between the child and his parents may be so pronounced that the parents do not believe that an outpatient plan could be maintained or could succeed. The adolescent may resist or fight against the parents' efforts to find help for him so that the parents could not take him easily to a clinic or the psychiatrist's office. The parents arrive at a point where they believe they cannot enforce simple requirements. Such parents are frequently oversolicitous, and it is as difficult for them to use residence as to support another treatment plan.

The relationship between the child and his parents may be so tenuous that the parents cannot become involved actively with him so as to sustain outpatient work. The adolescent may be unresponsive and withdrawn. With a patient of adolescent age this is not commonly a problem that has continued from early childhood. Parents are usually concerned about the possibility that the behavioral changes may represent the early indications of a psychotic reaction.

A parent who is unready to sustain an outpatient plan may himself be lacking in feeling or interest for the child. The parent who is indeed seeking to be rid of his responsibility for the child may select resident care rather than acknowledge fully his desire for foster placement.

The rejecting or negative expressions of parents are difficult to evaluate in preliminary interviews. The basic feeling potentials of the parents probably cannot be assessed finally until or unless there has been favorable change in the behavior and attitudes of the child. This means that treatment will be undertaken in many instances where there is doubt about the ultimate ability or intent of the parents. While parents are so perplexed, resident placement should not be allowed to create a situation in which the parents have turned over responsibility for the child and have severed their association with him.

Discouraged, pessimistic or bitter parents cannot provide adequate emotional support or encouragement as the adolescent enters into psychotherapy. It is artificial to expect such a parent to approach work optimistically. He can, however, comply with the practical requirements that are demanded by the treatment center. With most parents we should not expect significant changes in attitude until changes can occur in the patient. I am saying simply that unless the attitudes of the parents are quite superficial, they will not alter unless circumstances are different or until they have had an opportunity to work on their attitudes. The placement of the adolescent out of the home into residence does bring about an important change in circumstance, and parents may feel relieved to be free of immediate pressures. One can anticipate, however, that the discouraged attitude will continue until they can observe evidence of progress.

We accordingly are content in the initial phases of resident work with parents to direct our interest to the manner in which they comply with the practical and immediate requirements. These are designed to elicit active participation on the part of the parents in the establishment of a relationship with the Center staff and the maintenance of their association with the child. The formal requirements for the parents are outlined specifically.

In the preliminary or application procedure, they will come to Wilkes-Barre to see the Center and to learn of its way of working. Reports of earlier work or studies will have been obtained. The parents outline their ideas of the nature of the child's difficulties and of the dynamics of its development. When they are ready, an interview is held with the child and perhaps further psychological tests are performed. The parents are informed if we are prepared to accept the child. They are encouraged to take some time to consider whether this is the type of experience they are seeking for the patient.

If they decide to use the Center, they will be called upon to discuss the decision with the adolescent. He may be included in their deliberation, but we encourage parents to make the decision as their own rather than to have it come in compliance with, or be dependent upon, the wish of the patient. The adolescent comes to the Center with his parents to enter into a treatment relationship and a living experience that has been planned and arranged for him by his parents.

When there is not a parent who can fulfill in an elementary manner the practical requirements, the Center would require that custody be assumed by a foster care agency. The foster worker, as a representative of the agency, would carry out the procedures outlined above. The adolescent would look toward the agency to plan and care for him.

In residence, interest will be directed to what could be called an immediate definition of the difficulty. Interest is centered upon the manner in which the child establishes himself in the group situation. We are not concerned, initially, with eliciting conforming behavior. He will be assisted as he finds his way about the residence and as he becomes acquainted with the other children. He will learn the habitual routines. After a few days he will be entered into public school. Rather than directing him and imposing a desirable pattern of behavior, we try to help him establish himself according to his own tendencies. We help him examine how he is handling the various relationships into which he has been called upon to enter. Attention is directed to the feelings that have been aroused. The delineation of the nature of his behavioral tendencies and emotional reactions provides material for him to consider directly in his treatment interviews.

The immediate definition of the difficulty brings to the

fore a series of issues, only part of which the patient will introduce in psychotherapy. Though he is not compelled to discuss any particular problem in psychotherapy, he must discuss the practical aspects of his behavior with the resident professional worker who will emphasize certain features. Behavior and feelings which come repeatedly into prominence in his daily living will almost certainly be introduced by him into his treatment interviews.

The following material will illustrate what is meant by the immediate definition of the difficulty.

A fourteen-year-old girl had caused serious damage in several fires (several hundred thousand dollars). After a year of confinement to the grounds of a children's home, she demonstrated bizarre, hysterical behavior.

The following note was entered by a resident professional worker:

> Jean expressed her fearfulness and uncertainty by being negative and defiant. She objected to simple requirements such as going to bed when the time arrived. When she finally complied, she would move very slowly. She would scold resident workers or call them names. She would attract attention by outlandish behavior such as tearing up her napkin and eating it. She would not discuss her actions and when one tried to talk seriously to her, she would giggle or shout loudly. She said that people at the Center disliked her and were nice to her only because it was part of their job. She slowly reached a point where she could discuss her distrust and could acknowledge that she also felt hostile to people she admired. She found it difficult to like people and said that this might be because she found so much in herself to dislike.

The hysterical evasive quality of the girl's behavior was apparent in her manner of dealing with the resident staff.

As she examined with the therapist her distrust of the friendly motives of the staff and children, she could begin to acknowledge the fear that impelled her impulsive behavior.

The material was immediate and simple enough that she could have a sense of understanding it, whereas the earlier efforts to induce her to think about the fires and the unpleasant problems of her home had been unavailing.

The resident worker helps the adolescent note the patterns that evolve in his behavior, but does not attempt to carry discussions beyond a recognition of the manner in which he is behaving and the immediate feelings of which he can be aware. Delineating qualities in behavioral patterns in the setting in which they occur is the responsibility of parents in an outpatient procedure. In residence the adolescent established a new set of associations away from the family.

The definition of the difficulty in the immediate setting provides directional material around which work with both the adolescent and his parents becomes organized. In an outpatient service the parent is active in the early delineation of the issues that come into consideration. These arise out of the current experience of the patient and his parents. Their import is intermingled with the complex of feelings that exist in the intra-family group. In residence the individual inclination of the patient is more distinctly etched in his actions. He cannot project responsibility onto members of his family as he is in a new and removed set of interpersonal associations. The parents are also enabled to observe the behavior of the adolescent without being directly involved in the behavior.

The following case is illustrative.

A thirteen-year-old boy presenting a compulsive pattern was referred to the Children's Service Center after a year of psychotherapy on an outpatient basis.

He had been fearful in early childhood. First noted were specific fears, such as fear of bears, which continued until he was nine years old. At five he would not remain for lunch at nursery school. When he started grade school, it was necessary that he be compelled to attend. The fears seemed to fall into abeyance until his eleventh year.

He began to touch doorways as he passed. Other ritualistic movements concerned the parents so that they arranged for office psychiatric treatment.

There were absences from school when he complained of nausea. He would not return to school after the summer vacation. He would want his mother to carry out ritualistic movements with him or for him. He refused to allow his parents to be away from home.

The resident professional worker entered the following notes.

> Tom was an obviously fearful boy. He was annoyed when the children noticed his compulsive acts but insisted that he did not mind being teased.
>
> He was fearful of beginning school. On the way to be registered he wished that the school would burn, that they would be struck by another car or that the road would cave in. He threatened to jump out of the car. When enrolled, however, he attended. On several occasions he tried to avoid school by pretending that he was sick.
>
> Tom entered into conversations or play only when another child invited him. It was evident that he was not forming close friendships. He spent much time by himself.

In psychiatric interviews he revealed a great deal of hostile feeling. He challenged one by insisting that he would not eat, he would not go to school, etc. He seemed to expect the therapist to press him to eat or to enjoy himself. He could acknowledge that this was the kind of difficulty he was having at home and that his beginning in treatment did have to be a hostile one because that was the kind of feeling he injected into it. He demonstrated shyness and inability to express spontaneous feeling in the interview.

As he could examine the hesitancy with which he related to other children, he did not feel that he must continually discuss his compulsive behavior. He recognized that his compulsive acts were calculated to relieve a feeling of tension and also to control those about him. He was trying to maintain with his parents an infantile relation. He could see that at times he attempted to handle his fear by being hostile. He would risk interest in other boys only if he felt they were safe and accordingly he had few friends. He did not take part in many of the games that were played by boys his age. Shortly he reformulated his difficulty in immediate terms. He wanted to make friends and play with the others, but he was afraid to try. He would then turn to his compulsive actions. He performed them when he was troubled.

We can see how the immediate definition of the difficulty was established as his fear in personal relationships and his fear of new experiences, with some understanding of his desire to hold to a dependent relationship to his parents.

The parents had been afraid that the boy was psychotic. They gradually redefined the difficulty in their own minds as one of timidity. They could begin to see the need to encourage him in efforts to be more active and responsible. The father could indicate that he had had difficulty in college of a similar nature. He had partially worked through his difficulties but was still a timid and withdrawn person, much too shy for the requirements of his job and his social life.

A later note was entered in reference to the parents.

They have also developed a good measure of confidence in dealing with Tom. At first, they actually lacked belief that Tom could handle himself satisfactorily. The mother was the first to be encouraged by her capacity to limit Tom when he was anxious. She could see that she had been allowing him to do just about as he wished and that he was more comfortable when they did not allow him such extravagent expressions of feeling.

The definition of the difficulty takes into account the current interests and strivings of the adolescent. The evident tendencies are considered with the parents with the aim of assaying the patient's needs and his potentials. We are interested in evaluating the parents' expectations for their child and the manner in which they can participate in helping them materialize. In order to reach a satisfactory termination of resident treatment, the parents must approximate their aims for the adolescent with his actual capacities and must be able to supervise and assist in the living arrangement into which he goes after leaving the Center. (Over a period of fourteen years all of the children who have come into resident treatment at the instigation of their parents have returned to their homes.)

It is difficult to progress in treatment with a child where the ultimate wishes of the parents for him differ greatly from his potential. Children may be admitted into residence for psychological evaluation. If the parents persistently press for an impracticable goal, this should be recognized early.

A large number of children who are at borderline intellectually come to the attention of resident centers. The most common discrepancy between the adolescent's potential and the parents' concept of him derives from the discouraged attitudes of parents when the problem has been long-standing and attempts at treatment have failed or the parents' apprehensive attitude when the adolescent's behavior has been unusual or querulous. The common assumption is that the difficulty is an indication of a developing mental aberration.

That situation was illustrated in the case of Thomas. Only when the parents could observe over a period of weeks that he was attending school, and when they could learn through following his activities in the resident group and in psychotherapy that he saw his timidity and his fear in personal relationships as his basic difficulty, could their own interpretation of his difficulties alter. It was important that the boy's strivings and behavioral tendencies could be formulated with the parents in a manner which they could understand and with which they could sympathize.

In earlier years we tried too earnestly to engage parents in an affirmative manner in the early stages of resident treatment. This also led to too energetic efforts to help parents find solutions to their own personal difficulties. Today we are content at the beginning to have the parent comply with the practical requirements incumbent upon using our services. These include the establishment of regular interviews with the parents where there is an active consideration of the patients' family relations. Work with parents accelerates as changes are apparent in the patient's behavior. The early adjustment of the adolescent in the resident group is usually different in some respects from his behavior at home. The parents are then actively engaged as we arrive at what has been referred to above as the immediate definition of the difficulty.

Adolescence is a period of active development. The adolescent is responding to newly developed motives which derive from recently matured emotional drives as well as from an increased capacity for comprehension. He comes to this period with acquired patterned responses. Treatment which is directed primarily toward the dissolution of past difficulties will not assist him sufficiently in his search for ways to invest his new drives and interests. The treatment of the adolescent must accordingly be an active process directed toward what he is able to become.

One aspect of psychotherapy is the development of a better understanding of motives and patterns of behavior. Interest is centered on the way the patient handles himself in personal relationships and the feelings that are aroused. Attention to earlier experiences, feelings and attitudes may shed light on the nature of current tendencies. The ultimate aim is a more thorough appreciation by the patient of the nature and quality of his emotions and of the manner in which they are aroused and in which they influence his behavior.

Another aspect of psychotherapy might be termed a process of discovery for the patient. This is important in work with adolescents. It may follow a fuller understanding of the nature of feelings and motives. It also involves learning, which takes place in meaningful associations with other persons. The patient senses the feelings and attitudes of others and discovers new reactive capacities in himself. This is not effected solely in an imitative or sympathetic manner through which the adolescent comes to reflect the feelings and attitudes of those about him. A variety of new feelings will be stirred as he finds himself involved in meaningful relationships. In a resident treatment program important associations are established with the therapist, resident professional staff, and the other children in the resident group. Other associations are with his family and at school and in the community.

Gitelson (22) used the term "corrective psychotherapy." He emphasized the importance of dealing with ego factors rather than becoming concerned with the interpretation of hidden meanings. He talked of being didactic and enlightening, permissive and rationally controlling.

The successful management of the adolescent in the resident setting correlates with the degree to which he can be engaged in a meaningful consideration of the difficulties that confront him. He will demonstrate the patterns in behavior which led him into difficulties. For two or three weeks he is involved in becoming acquainted and establishing himself in the resident group, the school and community. During that time aggressive behavior is minimal. If issues can be met within the resident program, his antagonisms may be centered there. He will not have to turn his aggressive striving to the school and the community. Many adolescents who have demonstrated aggressive, hostile behavior can be carried in an open setting, such as the Children's Service Center, if one can actively engage their interest in dealing with significant issues in their actual life experience and in psychotherapy. The adolescent is going to express his urges and needs. If such expressions are not recognized in the residence in their incipient form, there will be more extravagant behavior and soon the difficulties will also manifest themselves in the community. To maintain work in residence with an adolescent over a prolonged period, his interest must become centered in his treatment interviews.

Let us consider the following case.

A fifteen-year-old girl came to the Center from a detention home after study at another clinic. The parents could not manage her at home because of her rebellious, delinquent behavior.

The parents had been divorced when the girl was one and a half years of age, and the mother remarried shortly thereafter. When Helen was thirteen years of age, she spent the summer with the paternal grandparents, where she met her father and at the end of the summer learned of his identity.

In the fall she would run away from home to the father's apartment. On one occasion she stayed with him for some two weeks and eventually, at her request, she was allowed to live with him.

Helen's difficulty had been evident prior to that summer. She failed in her school work. She avoided girls who were socially prominent. Smoking, truancy and talk about sex seemed to give her a feeling of achievement or independence, and she sought out friends who were misbehaving.

When she stayed with her father, who lived in a luxurious home in the downtown section of a large city, she was allowed to run the streets unsupervised.

The parents did not realize that she had come into open conflict with legal authorities until the father became ill and was hospitalized. It was learned that she had been placed in a sectarian correctional school. The parents allowed her to remain in the school. However, after several months she was discharged because she was inattentive in class, would not work, and was sarcastic and antagonistic to the teachers.

She returned to her mother's home in a fashionable suburb. When she was not allowed to date a boy who had a bad reputation, she ran away with him and was returned the following day by the police.

A few weeks later at a parent-teacher meeting at school, it was learned that she had been truanting and was still dating the boy of whom the parents disapproved. She again ran away but was apprehended in a few hours. The next day she disappeared. After a month it was discovered that she had gone to the city and joined a gang of boys and girls who had taken over an abandoned apartment and who had supported themselves through a variety of delinquencies. After a diagnostic study she was entered in a private school, but was discharged after one term.

The first night home she again ran away. She was held in a correctional home some months until she could be admitted to the Center.

The stepfather sincerely wished to contribute as actively and effectively as he could. He was quick to recognize that for a year they had seen Helen only when she had been in difficulty.

The mother openly rejected Helen and even directed letters to her using the real father's name instead of the family name (which was in fact the girl's legal name).

The mother and stepfather recognized that in allowing her to move back and forth between their home and that of her own father, they had allowed her to feel responsible to neither.

When she entered the resident group she was withdrawn and antagonistic. She had come into residence toward the end of the summer camp period. She stayed in her room. She responded in a negative manner to all suggestions. She would not go swimming, play games, work on crafts, do assigned chores, keep her room clean or dress neatly.

She cut her wrist with a razor blade. She said she had to do something because she was upset. She tried to prevent the cut from healing. When she realized it was going to heal, she cut herself in other ways. With a piece of glass she carved her initials into her hand. On another occasion she walked into the garbage pit (at summer camp) without shoes and cut her heel severely.

She talked of sex persistently.

After several weeks she began to participate a little in the activities of the group, but only when pressed to do so.

She would fight against practical and necessary issues. She didn't want to go to bed on time, have a bath every night, take a lunch to school, do her homework, go to the remedial teaching sessions, and she was uncooperative at school. There was repeated truancy.

She presented an extremely negative picture of herself during her early psychiatric interviews.

She felt children did not like her. She was ashamed of her sexual misbehavior. Yet she was preoccupied with thoughts of homosexual, perverse behavior. There was a strong urge to discuss homosexual knowledge with other children, using sordid terms.

Much of the early work revolved around her feeling that people could not and would not like her. There was a frank fear of school. She felt that she would not be accepted. It seemed that the only technique she had to establish a place for herself was in a fighting, misbehaving way designed to startle others. When she revealed sincere feeling, an abject feeling of worthlessness stood out.

This girl was carried in an open resident setting where she was free to have active associations in the community and to go to a public school. I believe that the satisfactory management was due to several factors. The parents were ready actively to assume responsibility for the girl's immediate and continued care. It was agreed that her real father would return her to her home immediately if she went to him without permission. There were a few weeks at summer camp prior to the beginning of school during which the girl's behavioral patterns could declare themselves. She was able to define her difficulty in her own mind in terms of attitudes and feelings in a manner that had immediate value for her. She had then begun to make use of her treatment interviews in a meaningful way. Her primary interests became centered in her associations in the resident program. Most of her antagonistic or troubled behavior was directed to persons within the residence.

The parents' attitude toward the girl underwent a series of changes. Initially the mother was bitter and resentful. The family placed a great deal of importance on the external indications of social position. The mother resented the embarrassment to which they had been subjected in the neighborhood and feared the unfavorable influence it would have on the younger children. The stepfather was genuinely fond of the girl and was ready to make a financial sacrifice to provide for her. In using residence each parent was relieved to be able to arrange a solution for the pressing problem of finding a way of caring for the girl. They had little optimism about Helen's eventually arriving at a satisfactory community adjustment.

After several difficult months, the girl gradually became conforming in the residence and at school. The parents, for the first time, could realize that Helen would eventually return to a community setting. Through repeated visits together in Wilkes-Barre, and also in their home, communication between the girl and her parents was greatly advanced. Now for the first time the parents could begin to consider practically the difficulties that would be involved in Helen's returning home. She was so seriously retarded in subject achievement that she would not be able to complete high school. This meant that she could not obtain employment that the family considered acceptable. Her scores on intelligence tests placed her in the dull-normal range. There was evidence that certain parents in the neighborhood continued to have such resentment that the girl would be handicapped in re-establishing herself. The mother, now, could talk freely of her discouragement about the girl and was not as bitter in her expressions of resentment.

As months passed and the girl's good behavior was maintained, it was evident that work was going to be effective. Helen was doing well in every area of her activities except school achievement. She was tolerated in school because she conformed with regulations, but she was not learning. After nine months in residence her effective use of psychotherapy was confirmed by her improved behavior and was documented when it was found on re-examination on psychological tests that she was scoring at average in tests of general intelligence.

The ultimately sound feeling of the mother and stepfather for the girl now became apparent. At the beginning of work, it would have been easy to conclude that there was a basic rejection of the girl. The parents had done a good deal of thinking about the factors that had influenced their attitudes toward Helen. As improvement in her behavior became established, they were able to recognize the changes she had effected, and to plan and work toward the day when she would return home.

They acknowledged that financially it would be impractical to have Helen live away from home. They recognized that she would need their supervision. They began to have her visit home more frequently and on those occasions arranged for Helen to have contact with their friends and neighbors so that people in the community could begin to see her as she was now. They had abandoned their pattern of concealing their concern for the girl from their close friends. They began to consider which work opportunities would actually be available. She was almost seventeen. Together, the girl and her parents decided that if she could obtain training without a high school diploma, she would enter a business college and study stenography.

A basis had now been reached for the girl's eventual discharge from residence. The parents had arrived at a point where they could assist and supervise her. There was a workable relationship between the girl and her parents. She had progressed a great deal in understanding the nature of her emotions and interests and had found that she could derive satisfactions within the bounds of social conformity. Moreover, the patient and her parents had already begun to deal with some of the difficulties which would eventually present themselves as she attempted to re-establish herself in her home neighborhood.

Effective psychotherapy will bring the adolescent to a new awareness of qualities of feeling and interest. This will be translated into efforts by him to alter his behavior and to handle himself differently in relationships with other persons. The recognition of incipient changes in attitude and in behavior is important in resident work. Technically the same principles are involved as were outlined above in the initial delineation of behavioral patterns following the adolescent's admission. After becoming acquainted with a patient in daily contacts, there is a tendency to accept a familiar level of behavior, and the resident staff must be alert to new differences in behavior.

As changes in the adolescent's pattern of behavior become evident and established, the parents will have an opportunity to see him in a new light. They have been engaged in obtaining a fuller understanding of the psychological aspects of his difficulties and the manner in which their own feelings and attitudes influence their relations with him. Newly discerned qualities in the patient will bring forth important responses from parents who then can be assisted in a better appreciation of their own motivation.

As the process unfolds, the patient's association with his family is maintained. The parents will visit regularly at the Center and he will have visits to his home. These visits home may be prolonged and more frequent as work progresses. His discharge from the Center does not bring him abruptly into a home setting from which he has become estranged. The ending of treatment comes as a natural step because the adolescent and his parents have prepared for it from the beginning of their experience with the treatment center.

The values in establishing a resident center as an intimate part of the community are perhaps apparent. The adolescent continues to attend a public high school with its varied extracurricular activities. He participates in organized social and recreational activities. He has a group of friends who play and visit with him at the Center and whom he visits in their homes. His adjustment is thus not effected in a restricted artificial setting. He will be better prepared to reestablish himself at home.

If children from a resident treatment center are to participate actively in community affairs, it is necessary to have the interest and sympathy of the community and particularly of the administrators of the various institutions such as school, church, group and recreational organizations, etc. A close working relationship with the schools is indispensable. More than a third of the patients who have been in residence at the Children's Service Center have had difficulties in school prior to admission so that they have been excluded from attendance. Experience has demonstrated that disturbed or troubled adolescents, when actively engaged in psychiatric treatment in residence, can be sent to public school and encouraged to participate in community activities.

Conclusions

1. Resident psychiatric treatment as practiced at the Children's Service Center is a way of providing individual psychotherapy for a child or adolescent.

2. Work is arranged at the instigation of the parents who will be actively engaged throughout the process.

3. The selection of cases is influenced by the nature of the relationship between the child and his parents. This relationship is affected by the nature of the child's difficulties and the basic attitudes of the parents.

4. The use of the actual life experience in the resident setting is discussed with comments on the role of the resident professional worker.

5. The manner in which work with the parents relates to the progress of the child in treatment is illustrated.

4

PSYCHOTHERAPY OF ADOLESCENTS
AT CLINIC LEVEL

SIDNEY BERMAN, M.D.

The problems of psychotherapy with adolescents in a mental hygiene clinic are strikingly different from those experienced with children and adults. This does not imply that there is an aura of unfathomable mystery surrounding the adolescent; rather, that the dynamics of adolescent behavior require special consideration. It follows, therefore, that certain prerequisites need to be met by the clinic, the patient, and those responsible for the patient, in order to establish a satisfactory therapeutic atmosphere.

The literature is replete with evidence that the specific forms of psychotherapy vary considerably from one clinic to another. This is due to several complex factors. There are differences in the type of service that different clinics render to different communities. The service may consist of practical help, advice or recommendations pointing to the need for environmental changes. Some clinics use group psychotherapy for adolescents; others rely mainly on supportive therapy, the objective being to strengthen the adolescent's defenses and develop emotionally corrective attitudes in keeping with his needs. Then, there is analytically oriented psychotherapy directed toward the resolution of internal conflicts, thereby strengthening the ego-adaptive functions and permitting character synthesis.

Among other factors which determine the nature and type

of psychotherapy, the clinic therapists possess diverse therapeutic skills and theoretical orientations. They also may demonstrate differences in ability to work with different adolescents. The unique psychological organization of the adolescent is such that neither the skills appropriate to children nor those used with adults will prove successful in the treatment of the adolescent. Moreover, the adolescent's particular disorder must be considered in order to determine the feasibility of treatment in a particular clinic. The relationship of the parents to the clinic has an unusual quality and their capacity to cooperate requires evaluation. This will be an important factor in determining success or failure in treatment.

The facilities of a mental hygiene clinic possess certain advantages and certain limitations. Where the services for psychotherapy are optimum, the clinic provides a treatment relationship in which the adolescent is helped in the natural habitat of his home, the school, his peers and the community wherein he lives. The direct relationship with his parents permits the adolescent in treatment to see them as they really are and to gain insight into the unworkable adaptive patterns he attempts to use in relation to them. The youngster frequently seeks help with behavior problems related to school and plans and aspirations concerning his educational goals. The pressure of his peers often bewilders him, and he wants advice so that he does not succumb to these anxiety-laden pressures. A need for a sense of identity with the community may be satisfied through community-sponsored groups such as the Boy Scouts, boys' club groups or athletic organizations, church groups, the Sea Scouts or air patrol and the like during the course of treatment. Some youngsters learn to dance, thereby expanding social contacts. Where treatment is clinic-centered, the adolescent has the opportunity to work out his problems in the setting where they have occurred and as he lives with them. Nevertheless, success in therapy is more closely related to the severity of the psychological disorder, the type of therapy used, and the therapist's knowledge and aptitude in working with these youngsters in their multiple phases of adaptation.

In further considering the advantages of a mental hygiene clinic in contrast to private practice and the residential treatment of adolescents, one must appraise the structure of the clinic and the manner in which it functions as an integral part of the community. It usually is located in the community in which the adolescent lives. The clinic has a close liaison with other community resources and services. The clinic's relationship to educational, recreational, welfare, law enforcement, religious, business and professional activities in the community is such that the staff members treating adolescents are in a unique position. They are able to help him appraise his problems realistically as they pertain to these areas of adjustment. More than that, the members of the clinic staff are cognizant of the prevailing cultural standards, how they influence mental health for better or worse. Therefore, they are able to help both the adolescent and his family resolve serious conflict by constructing and establishing reasonable standards or principles to live by. The patient's instinctual and social demands are not indulged in nor are they rigidly suppressed. These include such important problems as sibling relationships, school difficulties, patterns of eating, hours for arising and going to sleep, dating, the use of the car, week-end activities, family participation, smoking, masturbation, pornographic pictures, lying and deceiving others, and so on. It is apparent that the clinic's relationship to the parents, in a setting in which the family patterns of interaction are constantly in the picture, permits the parents to alter their reactions to the adolescent more appropriately in keeping with his needs and facilitates a more realistic modification of the adolescent's images of his parents. This will indirectly influence the unconscious forces operating in the superego. Often the therapist must assist in planning for, in supporting, or interceding on behalf of the adolescent in relation to educational, family and social problems and must contact teachers, school administrators, law enforcement officers and others. This requires the existence of a continuous relationship with the community. It demands the time and technique for such contacts which a clinic therapist is expected to have and which rarely is available to a therapist in private practice.

Most adolescents seen in the clinic are acutely faced with the direct and pronounced impact of forceful biological and psychological pressures which are difficult to cope with. They struggle within their limitations and restricted resources in their attempt to master these pressures. They lack the readiness and ease to replace former patterns of adaptation with more suitable teen-age outlets. The past value orientations stemming from the homes and communities in which they live, prove inadequate in adjusting to current needs, thereby resulting in much distress. These restrictive forces operate both at a realistic conscious level and at the unconscious level in the form of a disordered superego. Invariably the capacity for healthy identification is limited, and the adolescent feels that there is no one to whom he may turn for support or for affection, or to satisfy his need to express affection. In other words, there is no one to satisfy the adolescent's dependency and sexual needs in an acceptable way. The clinic therapist must support these needs. The goals of treatment, which are discussed later, are centered around strengthening the functions of the ego, that is, permitting character synthesis in keeping with the adolescent's age. This includes a more realistic orientation toward his parents, a more comfortable management of his biological tensions, and the channelizing of his creative and productive energies into rewarding social and educational goals. The resources and the versatility of the clinic services should be such that they effectively strengthen the adolescent's adaptive functions and enable him to achieve a reasonable measure of satisfaction.

The severity of the psychological disorder or the untenable environment the adolescent lives in may not make clinic service possible. Extremely disturbing behavior syndromes such as are seen in the excessively aggressive, asocial behavior of some adolescents, and perversions and psychoses where there is a serious impairment of interpersonal relations, create difficulties which cannot be adequately treated in most clinics. Also where the home cannot meet the adolescent's psychological needs or cannot give him the chance to work them out for himself, the obstacles to clinic treatment are insurmountable. On the other hand, psychosomatic syndromes, acute behavioral problems, and neurotic and some psychotic disturbances precipitated by the stress of the adolescent process combined with impaired ego strength have the best chance to be treated successfully in a clinic.

When the adolescent's internal conflict is intensive, though still not requiring hospitalization, treatment in private practice should be considered if this is financially feasible since the orientation of therapy is focused on the deep-rooted disturbances creating the psychopathology. More frequently, apart from the economic status of families, the choice of treatment in private practice should be based on the nature of the pathological disturbance and the limitations of the clinic service in managing the problem effectively. In actual practice, most clinics select the types of cases whom they can treat on a once-a-week basis. This is in keeping with the needs of the great majority of the adolescent patients. However, where the disturbance is severe as with some acting-out, asocial character disorders or psychotic and severe neurotic syndromes, the coordination of the treatment program by one person in private practice with an adequate time schedule for the patient and his parents is a more effective method of treatment. Most clinic facilities are such that they cannot accept the type of case that requires a time-consuming, analytically oriented approach or, on infrequent occasions, the application of psychoanalysis. The technical implications are too complex to be discussed in this context, but they are related to the mobilization of deep-rooted unconscious forces not only in the adolescent but also in the parents, most frequently the mother. In that sense, there are certain advantages if the therapist in private practice is able to manage the whole process. Then interviews can be arranged with one or the other parent, timed in relationship to the problems as they arise.

The need for a constant, controlled environment is a contraindication for attempting treatment in a clinic setting. A resident treatment center for adolescents presenting delinquency syndromes and severe psychotic and neurotic disturbances requiring constant care and treatment accepts the responsibility of a twenty-four-hour-a-day, regulated psychotherapeutic environment for the adolescent. The personal and social life, the educational and therapeutic planning are all oriented toward a total therapeutic milieu. The treatment objectives should be broad and all inclusive. However, when such a youngster is able to leave the resident treatment center, the utilization of clinic services may be indicated to support his rehabilitation.

Most clinics function on a voluntary participation basis, except for those affiliated with law enforcement agencies. At times, as much as one would like to be of help to the adolescent, it is impossible to do so. The adolescent, driven toward the acting out of impulses and unable to relate to any type of constraining experiences, cannot be relied upon to visit the clinic. Also, occasionally an impossible therapeutic atmosphere is created by the lack of cooperation of the parents who either withdraw the adolescent from treatment or undermine the treatment process itself because of their indifferent attitude or unconscious need to defeat it. This has to be accepted as an untenable treatment situation. Frequently, after a diagnostic appraisal of the problem has been made, the parents or the adolescent will not be ready actually to enter treatment, even though this is indicated. This feeling must be acceded to and the door be left open for future contact by them, if they are so inclined.

In the course of establishing and maintaining the treatment relationship the following five basic factors require consideration. These relate to the gathering of data for the diagnostic appraisal of the problem; the development of a collaborative relationship between the therapist and the patient; the management of resistances unique to this age group; the maintenance of contact with the parents in order to lessen tension, prevent interference and establish better harmony; and the termination of treatment based on limited, goal-directed objectives. These technical factors are oriented toward helping the adolescent achieve an optimum level of integration for his given age; he should be sufficiently free from entangling distortions of the earlier years and have a new emotional experience permitting the mastery and integration of powerful growth-directed forces. The techniques practiced in the mental hygiene clinic are related to three basic objectives. The first and most important is to improve the interpersonal relationship between the adolescent and his parents. Regardless of the methods used, this permits the necessary resolution of the unresolved dependency and oedipal difficulties. Without this, little hope for improvement can be expected. Second, the therapeutic experience supports the adolescent in adapting to the problems of day-to-day living with his peers. Third, it offers personal guidance and help in social planning for the present and future.

These factors are demonstrated in the case of a very quiet, unassuming, child-like girl of sixteen years who had difficulty in concentrating upon her school studies. She was extremely restrained, rather tearful, and offered no information spontaneously. There was a psychological suppression of menses, and a withdrawal from all social contact which had never been rich and rewarding. The mother was a powerful manipulator, very anxious and so controlling that the patient feared to do anything without her sanction and felt helpless without her support. The mother worried quite a bit about what people thought of her and carried this over to the critical appraisal of the activities of her two daughters who were totally dependent on her. The father's position in the family was that of participant who passively conformed to his wife's control and dedicated himself to his work.

The psychological examination showed her to be better than average and probably of superior intelligence, although the full-scale Wechsler-Bellevue test score gave her an I.Q. of 115, which appeared to be a minimal estimate. Concentration was poor; she was cautious and sensitive to implied criticism. The note of helpless despair and the response on the Rorschach suggested a neurotic depression. Emotional integration appeared poor and she tried to intellectualize emotions, fearing her responses to be explosive and hostile. There was some indication that during a period of her childhood she had been able to make a more healthy adjustment. This factor made the prognosis more hopeful than would appear from her current attitude of complete resignation. Her fantasy life was rich in spite of her efforts to conceal it. She showed creative and original thinking, and appeared to be dissatisfied with banalities. It was felt that if she were not so restrained and angry, she would be capable of excellent achievements. On the other hand, her silent resistance and defeatism presaged the need for a lot of tolerance and patience.

The girl was seen by the school counselor without success before coming to the clinic. The first therapist with whom she worked at the clinic showed strong anxiety because of her silence and tearfulness, placing the responsibility on her as to why she was there, so that she left his office with a feeling of futility. Through work with the mother, the patient was able to return to another therapist. The mother was seen at infrequent intervals in order to help her relinquish her control, her censorship, and her unrealistic social and personal standards which irritated the girl. The father was seen once so that he could clarify some of his own confusion about his daughter's behavior. A collaborative relationship was established with another therapist which gradually led to a clarification of the youngster's dependency upon her mother, and her feelings of helplessness and rage. Her scholastic achievement improved. The menses returned and became regular. She began having contacts with both boys and girls at school and in the social group at church, and eventually expressed her aspirations as to her future. She was seen once a week for four months. Once or twice a year over the past two years she has contacted the therapist about a specific problem as well as to review and share her successes.

When the clinic team obtains data for the diagnostic evaluation of the problem, this provides the opportunity to appraise the parents' reactions to the adolescent as well as the adolescent's own bewilderment in relation to his difficulties. Most often a parent or both parents are seen initially. Usually the parent who is able to furnish the most data is the mother and she is the one who is seen first. However, the inclusion of the father is highly important in order to obtain a clear picture of his contribution to the difficulties and to clarify his current involvements in the home. Most fathers want to be seen by the clinic, and they are eager for help in contributing constructively to the adolescent's needs and in the resolution of the youngster's difficulties. Frequently the parents also want to know how to present the problem of treatment to their child. It is important that the parents get help with this so that the adolescent feels that his parents show a positive interest in his problems. The adolescent often states that he isn't going to be seen by any psychiatrist and that he isn't crazy. If the parents have had a comfortable initial contact with the clinic in which their anxieties have been allayed, they will carry this over to the adolescent so that he will be willing to be seen, at least. From here on out, it is the nature of the relationship with the therapist which will decide what will happen in treatment.

The interview with the adolescent usually follows that with the parents and permits the therapist to prepare the adolescent for psychological testing. This initial contact is a crucial one, and the rapport established often will determine the subsequent treatment relationship. Psychological tests are extremely valuable, providing additional information about the adolescent's emotional and intellectual assets and personality organization. With the completion of the diagnostic survey, an evaluation can be made of the way in which the adaptive patterns and integrative forces in the personality of the adolescent operate and whether the home environment has the potentialities to meet his needs adequately. Then both parents are seen together or separately, depending upon which is most advantageous, in order to clarify the nature of the problem and initiate plans for treatment.

A factor of decisive importance in treatment is the adolescent's relationship with the therapist. It is recognized that certain members of the clinic staff possess greater skill than others in treating adolescents. There are some therapists who are successful in treating the inhibited, intellectualizing adolescent with an obsessional or schizoid character structure, and there are others who may work best with the rebellious, delinquent adolescent. The adolescent is not the type of patient who can be assigned at random to any staff member for psychotherapy. To follow such a policy is to invite a high percentage of failure in treatment. This indicates a need on the part of the clinic to select the therapist who is to work with the patient.

This was observed in the case of a youngster, sixteen years old, referred to a clinic from the Juvenile Court for stealing which was on a neurotic basis. He had previously been seen at another clinic where the therapist expressed an open dislike for the youngster who was sullen, resentful and defiant. The patient showed no ability to tolerate anxiety and attempted to shut the other person out of awareness. Apparently it was impossible for the therapist to tolerate the distrust and hostility felt by this patient. Under trying and difficult circumstances treatment was established in another clinic with another therapist; the parents were induced to participate in the treatment plans, otherwise the patient would not have been seen. Again the patient attempted to destroy the treatment relationship. However, the therapist's feeling for the patient and understanding prevented this. He succeeded in showing the youngster that his behavior was self-defeating and related to similar patterns in the past.

This shows that there is a significant factor which operates in addition to the therapist's possession of theoretical knowledge of the genetic and dynamic processes involved. This factor is the process of empathic communion which permits constructive collaboration and the capacity to appraise the adolescent's problems with objectivity. It reinforces understanding by providing a collaborative experience that strengthens the patient's ability to master his difficulties. In other words, this empathy creates an atmosphere of mutual trust and confidence which is necessary for treatment.

The intense anxiety of the adolescent has a quality which may easily create an antitherapeutic response in the therapist. It is, of course, important that the therapist can handle his own anxiety. The therapeutic relationship should provide the adolescent with an emotional milieu conducive to developing his integrative ego capacities. This does not mean that the patient is seduced by the therapist's charm or coerced by his rigid formality. Instead a middle ground is sought in the belief that both can establish a mutual respect for each other. Such collaboration helps to free the adolescent's psychic energies toward goals in keeping with realistic satisfactions.

However, if the therapist has a psychological blind spot as to his own adolescent difficulties, his relationship to the adolescent may be particularly anxiety-laden, because he then must defend himself against the adolescent's anxiety as well as his own. In this process the therapist may identify with the patient's emotional problems by taking sides with the adolescent against the parents or by sanctioning the unreasonable infantile demands of the patient. Under these circumstances, the adolescent is forced to use treatment in the service of his illness. On the other hand, the therapist may side with the parents and react with resentment and vindictiveness to the adolescent's hostility or evasive maneuvers (in which most adolescent patients are skilled), thereby causing treatment to collapse quickly. If the therapist is limited in his capacity to establish a meaningful relationship with the patient, it is problematical whether he can be of any help to the patient. In other words, the therapist's disturbed feelings and problems should not be added to the treatment situation.

The technique of therapy is based on a thorough knowledge of the dynamic and genetic psychological forces specific for the adolescent, on an understanding of the particular psychopathology present, and on an awareness of the unique physical forces and social factors involved. This permits better understanding, even though supportive therapy may be as much as the adolescent patient can accept at the clinic level. Supportive therapy uses suggestion, reassurance, education, and catharsis in order to help the adolescent handle his specific current problems more effectively. This type of therapy usually deals with the present life situation, selected by the adolescent or suggested by the therapist during the visit. Of course, there are some therapists who intuitively use these methods successfully. However, therapy based upon an understanding of the psychopathology and directed toward ego synthesis provides the opportunity to achieve a limited insight into the current emotional problem. Through collaborative investigation of the acute current difficulties the adolescent is strengthened in his adaptive capacity and judgment which was temporarily impaired. Where a more fundamental reorganization of the personality is indicated, it is necessary for the therapist to use psychoanalytically oriented psychotherapy permitting the resolution of the severe emotional problems stemming from earlier periods of life, as well as the current problems. This approach is used in severe neurosis or psychoses which may be seen in a clinic. The therapist focuses attention on those dynamic forces which asserted themselves earlier to create the current difficulty.

Usually, the patient and his family have not sought treatment prior to this period of the youngster's life. However, the psychological and biological forces at this time mobilize anxieties with which the patient cannot cope. The defenses which have up to adolescence appeared to be adequate now become ineffective. Repressed childhood material emerges as well as new symptoms related to the acute current problems. The bodily changes and powerful sexual impulses from within and the social forces from without place great stress upon the developing ego, which is at best fragile any way. There is a struggle to control the turbulent sexual drives and aggressive impulses. The emancipation from internalized parental controls as well as actual emancipation from the parents is impaired, and the adolescent's aspirations toward psychological and physiological maturity are blocked. Where the relationship to the parents is primarily a hostile one, with either too rigid a conscience or no conscience, the old ineffective patterns of childhood will operate, and further the development of neurotic, psychotic, or characterological disturbances. Although the adolescent ordinarily repudiates on a conscious level his relationship to parents and society, his dependency status and oedipal conflict are resolved only gradually with increased ego strength and goal-directed behavior. The involvement with the parents on an infantile and childhood level is slowly abandoned, permitting the gradual repression and substitute gratification of internally determined impulses, within the limits set by reality and without too marked a violation of the restriction established by his conscience. The process is a gradual one, extending over several years, depending on the environment in which the adolescent lives, for it takes a long time to discard the old patterns and develop more effective new ones.

Rarely does the adolescent seek help for himself. Nor does he quickly become engaged in treatment on a collaborative basis. Either the parents, the school or the court have become disturbed by the behavior of the patient and request intervention, usually because of an acute problem. The youngster is often distrustful, feels humiliated and as though he were an evil creature. This is understandable for the adolescent's conception of himself is impaired. The patient is struggling with internalized and real objects, which are punitive and which interfere with his capacity to master the sexual drives and his ability to emancipate himself gradually without overwhelming anxiety. He finds it hard to accept as his own the internalized controls and values because his parents have been too intolerant or indifferent to them, causing a negative identification against which he fights. Also, he knows nothing but distrust for those who endeavor to help him establish controls with which he could live more comfortably. Since he cannot get close to those with whom he has serious problems, both at a conscious and unconscious level, he feels the same way toward those who seem to act as surrogates for his parents. Still, it is within the treatment relationship that the resolution of the distorted dependency ties and the oedipal situation require some measure of closeness on a warm, understanding, firm, tolerant basis, if the youngster is to achieve a satisfactory reorganization of his personality.

The diagnostic evaluation of the problem is a necessary procedure not only to formulate the problem, but also to accept the limitations as to what can be done in certain cases. Such a study has therapeutic value, whether the patient continues to be seen in the clinic or is referred elsewhere, for it provides a working basis upon which to proceed to the next step. When it is obvious that treatment in a clinic setting is not indicated, I personally feel that other plans should be recommended, otherwise we would only add failure to what already has failed. Yet at times we yield to the entreaties of the patient's parents, the school or court only to confuse further the dilemma and to increase the resentment felt by all concerned.

It is important to obtain the approval and support of both parents, regardless of the degree to which they participate in treatment. Without this, the adolescent's resistance and reluctance may be even greater. Also, where the parents are uncooperative, either wittingly or not, they will tend to negate the effects of treatment and thus make it untenable. Where it is not possible to obtain the cooperation of the parents due to their own emotional difficulties and it is felt that the adolescent cannot make a change in such an environment, it is better to postpone treatment rather than to get into a situation which will lead to obvious failure and disappointment. At times it is possible to recommend treatment of the parents concurrently with treatment of the adolescent, and there are advantages to this. Also, placement in an environment which appropriately meets the adolescent's needs may be indicated. The placement or postponement of treatment should be considered where the adolescent's ego organization is weak and the behavior patterns are so strongly self-defeating or destructive that they prevent the establishment of therapeutic rapport. Some adolescents will show a pseudo-independent desire to avoid treatment, and guard themselves so that treatment is impossible.

Often parents do not want to participate actively in therapy, especially if the youngster's presenting symptom is delinquent behavior. In such cases one can frequently observe a resemblance between the problems of the patient and those of the parents. They frequently expect the adolescent to assume the full burden of responsibility. This is particularly

true where the adolescent's symptoms represent serious unconscious problems of the parents which they have not been
able to master.

A mother visited several private child psychiatrists and
also sought help from a clinic. She was too busy with her own
occupational activity to find time to give to her daughter,
although it was not necessary for her to work. The mother
was aware that this child did not have someone to care for
her or love her. The daughter, thirteen years old, made all
sorts of absurd demands on her mother. If the mother did
not fulfill these demands, she would make abortive suicidal
attempts, wreck the house while her mother was away, or she
would leave home. If the mother fulfilled these demands, the
youngster quickly lost interest in what she had received. This
mother also used money to buy the concern of others and
she was terribly dependent on them for emotional support.
She expected the maid to care for her daughter as well as
herself. Her daughter felt unloved, lost in her relationships
to others, and asked unreasonable things from everyone, including the therapist, to prove she was not loved. This girl
struggled to repress her violent and angry feelings through
eating. There was much confusion about sex and guilt about
her sexual impulses. However, at home she would succumb
to her explosive feelings, and run away repeatedly or miss
appointments. Just as the mother ran to men to assist her
with advice about her difficulties, the daughter ran off with
strange young men who got involved with her although she
was obese and unattractive. Inpatient hospital treatment was
recommended, but the mother could not follow through with
this until the situation became unbearable over a period of
two years. Both mother and child sought material things in
life which never satisfied their emotional needs. Both felt
despair, unloved and helpless, and both sought satisfaction
away from the home. They could not master their dependency needs and sexual impulses, and both would respond to
each other with violent rage and cruel accusations. The
mother succeeded in persuading many therapists, some of
them twice, to take on her daughter's treatment before, following a crisis at home, she could accept the need for institutional care for her daughter.

The situation is paradoxical. On the one hand, at a conscious level the parents complain about the behavior of the adolescent, and, on the other, unconsciously perpetrate their basic distorted relationships with the youngster because their child's problem has become intimately linked with their own which they wish to avoid. Often the adolescent's behavior represents the parents' value orientations and reflects the unconscious difficulties they have not been able to integrate adequately themselves. Not being able to help themselves, they cannot help the adolescent. Nevertheless, constant communication with both parents must be maintained by the clinic team to provide information, to prevent the parents from blocking the progress of treatment, and to help them find more successful ways of dealing with the adolescent's wishes and demands. This contact frequently creates greater tolerance in the parents and becomes a rewarding, positive, educational experience for them.

Once treatment has begun, we are faced with the problems of communication, the content of the interviews, and the nature of the resistances. The manner in which these problems are managed in the psychotherapeutic setting is determined in great part by the therapist's personality and his abilities. The extent to which the therapist is able to understand the adolescent is related to the degree of self-awareness he possesses, particularly the extent to which he has resolved anxiety related to his own adolescent problems. The adolescent tests the therapist's limits of tolerance and his psychic integrity, just as he does with his parents.

If the therapist has merely a theoretical intellectualized concept of the adolescent process, this represents a defense, a psychological scotoma, which may prevent the patient from clarifying his own problems. Moreover, the patient may mobilize such intense anxiety in the therapist as to cause him to be indifferent, hostile, and even to break off therapy. The adolescent is quick to exploit weakness in the therapist, just as he is with his parents and teachers. He rapidly detects the therapist's attitudes—whether he is indecisive, anxious, shaken with doubts, hates or respects the patient. However, where the therapist is able to provide emotional stability and a meaningful appraisal of the adolescent's current problems, this experience has a better chance of having an enduring effect on the adolescent's personality.

The verbal and nonverbal language used in treatment by the adolescent is unique, to say the least. It is neither the shared language of the child, nor does it have the informative quality of the adult. It has a special quality and style characteristic of the adolescent peer group. Language communication between an adult and adolescent is difficult at best. But in an adolescent who is emotionally disturbed, distrustful and suspicious, it is even more of a problem. Therefore, the therapist's choice of words, the tone of voice, the ease with which speech is formulated, and even the body tensions subtly convey to the patient whether the therapist is comfortably related to the adolescent or not. The quality of the communication requires sympathetic understanding free from artificial restraint or seductive exuberance.

Bringing adolescents to treatment against their will, immediately creates a situation in which they cannot talk freely. Initially, they feel that they are culprits who are indicted and disapproved of. Therefore they are defensive, distrustful, fearful and bewildered. They feel out of favor and deeply hurt because of what has happened to them. Regardless of whether they are overtly truculent and defiant at one extreme or seemingly compliant and reserved at the other, they enter treatment with misgivings and are reluctant to talk about their feelings with the therapist. However, where there is a positive, empathic relationship, the adolescent gradually will put aside his reserve and caution, and begin to see in the therapist an ally who is helpful and understanding in a constructive way. Then the knowledge and the values possessed by the therapist meet the patient's reality needs and become desired by the adolescent. At the same time the verbal language becomes less constrained and directed to problems the patient is concerned about. Even at that, the verbal responses will have a restrictive quality, but they will be a closer approximation of the problems the adolescent is struggling with.

At first the adolescent usually talks about his experiences at school, in extracurricular activities or with a teacher. These communications refer only indirectly to his real problems. In general, the adolescent does not respond to attempts at depth-psychological investigation or dynamic interpretation. If these are used, the treatment relationship may be destroyed. Attempts at uncovering repressed affects related to past life experiences are futile. Instead, there is a need to disclose gradually the present psychic difficulties in a way which can be endured by the adolescent and which is meaningful and constructive to him. It is only through the clarification and resolution of these problems at the adolescent level that the underlying dependency and oedipal conflicts can be adequately resolved.

In fact, it is difficult for a time to get at the content of the immediate life experiences which are disturbing and which need to be put into proper perspective if the adolescent is to be helped. He is adept at talking about things which are tangential and only gradually discloses the problems he has in present relationships. Current attitudes as they are expressed gradually lead to the exploration of current conflicts, especially those with important people with whom he lives, his mother, father, and the other children in the family.

This process frees him and enables him to cope with the intense psychological and physiological forces in a healthier way and convert his dependency and sexual relationships of childhood into more appropriate channels of expression. When this is achieved, the adolescent will elaborate more fully and not in a defensive way his problems and plans as well as his aspirations for the future. Now the information is shared in a collaborative relationship rather than used as a defense. Frequently, up to this point they have no healthy future goals in keeping with their ability and they are so overwhelmed by present anxieties that they are unable to direct their psychic activity toward future plans.

The following data are from a boy fifteen years of age: "Today in school a boy, usually my good friend, comes up to me and starts playing around. He started marking all over my white shirt with a pencil. He just laughed and thought it was funny. I felt like a big sissy and a coward and walked away and came back a little later. And he did it again. I told him to quit it and then the bell rang. Instead of wanting to fight him or something, I just felt like crying. But I didn't. I just felt mad and knew I couldn't fight him. I felt so nervous and depressed that I felt like killing myself. The boy just looked at me and laughed. Later on he asked me if I was mad at him and I said a little. Then he acted normal and friendly again, but I feel like a coward and I just can't live this way. All the other boys walk all around normal. They are physically good but I don't know about myself. [He is 5′ 9″ tall and a rather attractive youngster, although when he was first seen he appeared to be immature.] I just can't stand it. I feel bad and I am just afraid of those boys. I can't understand it but I have always been weak and all the boys are strong. Anyway, I'm just afraid to fight. I don't know why. I hate the school and I hate people and that is about the way I feel. I just feel like coming home and staying away from people. Doctor, that isn't good. You've got to help me." There was talk about handling his problems by using barbells. The early hours were filled with constant complaints about the teachers and students, and ideas of stopping school. He seemed to express the same sense of futility to the therapist that he felt in relation to his parents. Gradually, the interviews explored his problems at home. His mother was an extremely dependent person who overprotected and seduced him to be close to her. She constantly called to check on him when she was out. She also exploited her husband, demanding that he minister to her emotional and physical needs. The father was violent in his feelings about his son's dependence on mother who overprotected him. The patient also was adroit in upsetting his father and much of his hostility was spent at this. As his unworkable dependency and oedipal relationships in the home were clarified, he no longer talked about school problems, his grades were excellent and he began to make plans to go to college for which he was well equipped. He got part-time jobs, joined a boys' social and fraternal organization, and found great rewards in friendships with both boys and girls. At first he had a difficult time adjusting to girls, making unreasonable demands upon them which were similar to those he made with his mother. Slowly he learned how to relate to them so that they showed a natural adolescent interest in him. Actually, in this case, the father and not the mother was the parent who was available and seen at frequent intervals. This permitted the father to develop a better workable relationship with his wife and both of them were able to cope with the attempts of the patient to upset and divide them through his self-centered demands. The violent hostility which was suppressed outside the home broke out in the home and gradually was resolved there, especially in relation to his father.

It is necessary for the adolescent to see people, especially his parents, as they really are, with all their weaknesses and assets. This reorientation of the adolescent to his environment with a greater tolerance for those about him is an extremely important aspect of therapy. It is only by means of the therapeutic situation that the adolescent develops this objectivity and tolerance. This new insight into what the people around him really are like may, on the one hand, cause some resentment and disappointment although now it is at a conscious level. On the other hand, it comes as a refreshing revelation. This allows the patient to achieve a constructive reorganization of the hostility toward the parents and other important people. With this it is possible to reorganize the sexual and aggressive drives in the direction of

achieving satisfaction in accord with the opportunities afforded by reality.

Where the therapist is skilled in dream analysis, and a
positive therapeutic relationship exists, the adolescent will
share his dreams for study. Dreams give extremely valuable
information about the underlying mental activity. But interpretation should be made only to strengthen the adolescent's current adaptive capacities. To use this powerful
source of information in any other way is dangerous and
contraindicated. The objective of therapy at a clinic level
is to strengthen the ego, and not to become involved in the
infantile and childhood conflict.

Adolescents notoriously attempt to manipulate the treatment hours. In the beginning of treatment, less than one
hour a week is meaningless. However, attempts often are
made to keep the interviews as infrequent as possible, and
these endeavors reflect the intensity of resistance. The patient also may miss hours and offer inappropriate excuses.
Anything less than one interview a week in the early phase
of treatment will be meaningless to the patient. The old
defenses will continue to operate. So many adverse situations
will pile up between appointments that the therapeutic
process will be nullified. Then the adolescent's activity is
directed to defeating the therapist, in about the same way as
he has done this to others.

One youngster, fifteen years old, attempted to defeat treatment by coming late or by trying to miss the hour in exactly
the same way he would reluctantly agree to do chores at
home and then find an excuse to get out of them or be late
for school. It was possible to show him that this was a self-
defeating maneuver which would only make treatment meaningless, and to make him aware of the similarity of this irra-
tional behavior and that which went on between him and his
parents. This quickly led to expressions of the resentment he
felt toward his mother because of her nagging, unreasonable
and inconsistent demands, and his father who was quite inde-

cisive in these matters. Gradually he found more practical ways of dealing with this problem.

There are occasions when it is necessary to see the adolescent more than once a week, especially if he acts out on a neurotic basis and creates difficulties from which he cannot extricate himself. However, usually there is a reluctance to be seen more than once a week. As treatment draws to an end, he may wish to be seen once every other week or once a month, gradually weaning himself from the relationship and establishing his own autonomy. As a rule, the more frequent the interviews and the longer the treatment, the more constructive and enduring are the changes in the psychological organization of the adolescent.

Silence in the treatment hours can create a troublesome situation for some therapists and make them overanxious. This silence represents great anxiety and distrust or hostility. The tendency to restrict verbal communication places the burden of responsibility on the therapist to stimulate productivity. Such behavior may indicate a youngster's reluctance to acknowledge that he has a problem—a situation which in itself is embarrassing and humiliating. He may resort to silence also in an attempt to control and master his impulses. To put them into words would be too frightening. He is ill at ease because of the necessary repression and yet feels he is forced to produce. It should be remembered that the adolescent also is frightened by the silence and requires help to get over his distrust, defiance and need to maintain a distance between himself and the therapist. It is the therapist who encourages the adolescent to go first to material that can be safely discussed, and then gradually to the current problems causing resentment and vindictiveness. The nature of the silence first is explored in terms of what it means to the patient in relation to the therapist.

The clash between the desire for emancipation and the

childhood taboos and implicit and overt restrictions create much confusion, hostility and resentment. Some youngsters may withdraw with a feeling of resigned helplessness, using obsessional rituals to contain their conflicts and anxieties as well as to obtain spurious gratification. Others cling to their parents with a catastrophic helplessness coupled with resentment that breaks out from time to time when anxiety over a difficult situation is mobilized. This often is seen in the schizoid youngsters. Still others externalize the hostile aggressive drives in an attempt to repudiate the past from which it is impossible to escape. In any event, it is necessary to forewarn parents that the adolescent will get worse in some ways before he can improve. This preparation enables the parents to be more tolerant and stable in the face of these overt expressions of conflict which must be worked through.

However, the impulse to "act out" problems, particularly if intense, is a serious sign and may cause treatment to end in failure, unless the therapist succeeds in discouraging it through verbalizing its meaning as a self-defeating power manipulation. This behavior may jeopardize the welfare of the patient and the therapeutic relationship. Such youngsters show a serious impairment of their psychological organization and may get into painfully dangerous situations. They tend, through their actions, to cope with deep-seated psychological difficulties and show little ability to control or restrict their behavior. The parental restraints with these youngsters usually have been inconsistent, too lax in some ways and too severe in others. Such parents usually have had a hard time controlling their own irresponsible, impulse-driven behavior and have not been able to help the adolescent regulate his. The clinic needs to include the parents in the treatment situation in order to support them and also to obtain their assistance in helping the adolescent. Occasionally, these destructive impulsive acts make treatment untenable; when there is an absence of regulatory restraints in the family and the adolescent, placement should be considered where feasible.

Just as these patients attempt to suppress their sexual impulses, or to find surreptitious gratification for them, so, too, in therapy, it is difficult to communicate verbally their reactions to this powerful drive. The repressive forces of childhood are reinforced in an attempt to contain this drive so that it is subject to vigorous restraint. The adolescent reacts to this biological surge with secret ways of alleviating tension and with feelings of guilt and self-punishment. This attempt to master the sexual drive by dissociating it or by various guarded acts has a devastating impact on the adolescent's adjustment. There is a reluctance to investigate the feelings and thoughts associated with the sexual drives. Nevertheless, the indirect ways in which this problem is expressed by the adolescent permit the therapist to bring it into the youngster's awareness. By discussing it with respect and devoid of humiliation, he enables the patient to integrate his strivings as an acceptable part of himself. The cues are obtained from the patient, and the patient is furnished only with information he is able to accept. Usually information related to the sublimation of these drives into socially acceptable channels is sought by the adolescent. At times they express a need for information to clarify their past distorted concepts related to sexuality.

The basic relationship to the parents has not provided steady emotional growth so that the process of emancipation has permitted the conscious dissolution of the dependency needs and the repudiation of oedipal strivings. The parental relationships have not been based on fair decisions with respect and regard for the adolescent's needs. As a result we see basic deficiencies in the internal controls of the adolescent. The controls are not built on inner harmony. The controls may be too lax or inconsistent, precipitating rebellious behavior with verbal and physical assaults on parents, attempts to run away, and excessive defiance. A sixteen-year-old adolescent, when he could not get the family car or find the food in the icebox which he wanted, would have violent temper tantrums in which he either hit his mother or broke any object he could put his hands on. The father feared the boy's violence and the mother was inconsistent, either nagging him or submitting to his overpowering dependency requests.

The control also may be too rigid and oppressive so that the resultant difficulties find expression in psychosomatic complaints, compulsions, phobias, conversion symptoms, depression or schizophrenic reaction patterns. All of these represent attempts at reinforcing the repression of drives that are too strong and difficult for the adolescent to cope with.

As the adolescent is able to handle his problems more effectively, his inherent capabilities are freed and his expanding interests become observable. He tends to function more efficiently in school, and more comfortably with his teachers and classmates. There also is an expansion of his social interests, and he begins to seek heterosexual relationships as well as friendships with boys in his own peer group. Now he neither submits or dominates, but becomes an integral part of the group life. With the mastery of problems previously avoided, he seeks challenging new experiences and no longer succumbs to the feeling of inevitable failure and defeat.

On occasion, the disappearance of the symptoms constitutes a return of the repressing forces, indicating that the patient wants to stop treatment because it creates more anxiety than he can handle. The fact that this is not improvement based on a mastery of the problems is evident because there will not occur concomitant improvement in the family, social and educational spheres. It is a flight into health which occurs only in the treatment situation and indicates a strong resistance to treatment.

However, once the adolescent has obtained sufficient help from the treatment relationship, he is ready to leave the therapist and make his own way. Treatment usually does not last very long, for the adolescent is as eager to emancipate himself from the therapist as from his parents. It is important for both to agree on ending treatment, with an understanding that if problems arise in the future, they can get together again. On this basis, it is possible for the adolescent to call the therapist for an appointment or two to work out a specific problem. Patients occasionally return on their own for a longer period, this time knowing that they are not bound by the demands of others, and even participate more effectively in the psychotherapy, because it is something they want instead of something the parents or society demands. When they do return, usually parents or social problems do not grant them the right to utilize the gains made and precipitate a recurrence of symptoms or the patient becomes involved in problems because of unresolved conflicts. The objective of psychotherapy is to permit the adolescent to achieve adequate synthesis of his personality, that is, effectively control the adolescent impulses and conflicts for his given age level so that he is freed for normal emotional growth with the opportunity to create for himself healthier social and educational experiences which lead to maturity.

The emphasis in this paper has been upon the treatment of the adolescent in the mental hygiene clinic. Actually both the mother's and father's participation goes hand in hand with it and makes up the total therapeutic situation.

5

PSYCHOTHERAPY OF ADOLESCENTS BY PEDIATRICIAN AND PSYCHIATRIST AT COMBINED CLINIC AND INPATIENT HOSPITAL LEVEL

HERBERT I. HARRIS, M.D.

and

FELIX P. HEALD, M.D.

The Adolescent Unit at the Children's Hospital in Boston is a general medical clinic for young people between the ages of twelve and twenty-one. They are seen in this Unit for any problem from diabetes to sprained knees, from dysmenorrhea to scholastic failure. In short, the Unit specializes only in that it confines its attention to members of this age group; for them it operates as a general practice clinic. The Unit's policy is to focus on the person, and to attempt to meet all his needs rather than to be concerned chiefly with, or to limit treatment to, a specific disease or organ. This report discusses the policies and philosophy behind the services to adolescents and training program for physicians which that Unit offers, particularly as these relate to the management of emotional disorders.

At his first visit a patient is assigned to a physician who will continue to be his physician throughout the entire time he is treated in the Unit. Should his physician feel special knowledge is needed, a group of consultants in all specialties is available. When such is the case, however, the consultant comes to the patient, and sees the patient *and* his physician so that both benefit: the patient from the expert's opinion and the physician from the consultant's teaching.

One of the Unit's major interests is the development of physicians' understanding of adolescent personalities and of skill in managing their psychosomatic disorders. Each physician in the Unit is assigned to a psychiatrist who acts as teacher and supervisor for all problems in diagnosis, management and psychodynamics which any patient presents. Every effort is made to teach these physicians how to approach patient care from the psychodynamic point of view, to recognize and treat minor emotional problems, to recognize those emotional patterns that require a psychiatrist's skillful management, and to appreciate the emotional component that is part of every organic disorder.

It is our aim to have the general practitioners, pediatricians, and internists working in the Unit gain both an intellectual concept of emotions as they relate to general medicine, and to acquire those techniques of psychotherapy which they can use daily in the practice of medicine. Increased knowledge of personality development enables the physician to utilize it in handling all his patients, whether they have a purely emotional disturbance, a physical illness, or a mixture of two. As we all know, a doctor-patient relationship becomes more and more effective as a physician acquires a psychotherapeutic attitude and learns to understand his patient as a *person* and not merely as a *problem* in diagnosis and treatment. We feel that such an approach is desirable with all patients and that it is essential if one is to be successful with adolescents.

Furthermore, if the personality of the patient is ignored, the etiology of the patient's symptoms cannot be clearly understood. Abdominal pain or headache, for example, are often encountered in the absence of a demonstrable lesion in gastrointestinal roentgenograms or an abnormal electro-encephalogram, but when an attempt to understand the patient's personality is included as a part of the medical appraisal, evidence is often found to explain the patient's symptoms.

The following cases illustrate clearly how a strictly medical approach will fail to unravel presenting symptoms.

Case I

This sixteen-year-old girl was referred to the Unit for persistent epigastric pain. Thirteen months previously she had had a series of fainting episodes over a two-week period: following these she was admitted to a hospital for a one-week period of observation. This extensive medical work-up included a basal metabolism, electrocardiogram, and an electro-encephalogram. All were normal.

Following this hospitalization her fainting attacks ceased, and she remained well until eight weeks prior to her first visit to the Adolescent Unit, when she developed mid-epigastric pain. This symptom was treated with various antispasmodics, and when these gave her relief, her pain shifted to her chest. This symptom persisted, and she was again admitted to a hospital for a five-day period. A second intensive gastrointestinal survey was negative. At that time peptic ulcer was suspected, the tentative diagnosis of mesenteric adenitis was made, and she was referred to our Unit for further study.

At her initial visit she told us that she had had insomnia for the previous eight weeks, and in describing her epigastric pain said, "My stomach feels tied up in knots." She also talked about difficulties at home with intense emotion and at great length. Her physical examination was negative.

All medication was discontinued, and further medical studies were deferred, pending further evaluation of her personality and her emotional status after a very few visits at which she discussed her problems. Her gastrointestinal symptoms disappeared and she has been symptom-free for a year. It was clear to us that this girl's gastrointestinal symptoms were psychosomatic, and that attention to her emotional difficulties with an opportunity for her to express her feelings permitted her a prompt and rapid response, whereas the previous strictly medical approach had failed.

A patient's symptoms and the emotional problems accompanying them must be approached in terms of their origin, development, and meaning. It is not enough to approach a patient's complaints from the purely organic aspect and, if after extensive laboratory tests no pathology can be demonstrated, to label the patient neurotic by process of elimination and to suggest a referral to a psychiatric clinic. This narrow approach does not utilize our present knowledge of personality and is often unsuccessful in determining the origin of symptoms. When a patient comes to a physician with a specific complaint, he comes for a diagnosis and for treatment of his symptoms. He is not concerned whether his symptoms are organic, but is asking for help. On the other hand, when a total approach including personality evaluation is utilized, the physician is able to take a positive stand regardless of the origin of symptoms, whether they are those of an organic disease with anxiety about its effects, or purely emotional, or a mixture of the two.

The next case history indicates that a knowledge of the adolescent's personality and a due regard for both the physical and emotional factors in illness and the relationship between them helps to prevent erroneous diagnosis.

Case II

This sixteen-year-old girl complained of nervousness, fatigue, inability to sleep, and recent failure in school. Her mother had taken her to several psychologists because she believed her symptoms were psychological in origin. Their findings showed that hostility toward the mother and her mother's previous hospitalization for ruptured disc were responsible for the girl's present symptoms. They recommended psychotherapy. The mother said that her daughter had had many emotionally traumatic experiences since the age of twelve: six months previously the mother had been operated on for a ruptured intervertebral disc, and she believed this hospitalization had upset our patient.

Our patient was tall, attractive, and alert. She talked freely and without tension. Though she seemed to believe she had many things the matter with her, her manner in talking about them was typical of a well-adjusted girl and not at all that of a neurotic person. Her interpersonal relationships seemed satisfactory, and her general demeanor seemed inconsistent with her symptoms.

Her physical appearance produced an impression in striking contrast to that gained of her personality. She did not look well. Subsequently her physical examination and her laboratory tests confirmed the initial clinical impression of hyperthyroidism. In this instance, had the physician not been familiar with adolescents, or had disregarded the emotional and physical aspects of his patient's disability, he might very well have overlooked the inconsistencies between the patient's behavior and her symptoms.

In our Unit the physician is given training in the dynamics of personality with special reference to the adolescent. He gains this knowledge by working with adolescent patients, and by having at his disposal a psychoanalyst whose specific task is to teach normal personality structure and characteristics as well as the deviations from the "normal." This enables the physician to have a clearer picture of the doctor-patient relationship and to be more aware of his role in dealing with these young people. With this awareness the physician is better equipped to handle the rebellious, the resentful, the frightened, or the tense adolescent in the highly important first visit.

Working under the supervision of a psychoanalytically-trained psychiatrist, physicians are also helped to gain insight into their own attitudes toward patients, and to discover both some of the less obvious motives for their own behavior and also the reasons behind their professional activity and its satisfactions and disappointments. Those physicians who desire and are temperamentally able to follow this approach with their adolescent patients find this supervision invaluable. Reading about the treatment of emotional problems and personality development is not enough. There is no effective substitute for the actual training and supervision by a psychiatrist who is familiar with adolescents. Physicians so trained will then be able to recognize and treat many minor emotional disturbances. They will also recognize serious emotional disturbances and refer these patients and others whose management requires expert care by the psychiatrist.

The well-oriented pediatrician or internist who is able to detect and treat minor emotional problems is in a position to do something at a time near their onset, a time we all know them to be most amenable to treatment. This kind of training for the internist, pediatrician, and general practitioner places them in the forefront of the preventive mental health movement. It is striking and heartening to observe how promptly most physicians become sensitive to even somewhat obscure emotional disturbance and how effective they are in utilizing this new knowledge.

Symptoms which have eluded previous medical explanation are more readily understood when the influence of the emotions on physiological and pathophysiological processes are seen in this new light. Often symptoms such as abdominal pain, or cramps with nausea, or vomiting on the first day of the menstrual period can be explained only by gaining an understanding of the patient and of what she is trying to say with her symptoms. Needless and repetitive laboratory examinations are eliminated if the physician always tries from the very first to understand and know his patient and does not focus exclusively on his or her disease or symptom.

Case III

This fourteen-year-old girl had well-regulated diabetes mellitus for fifteen months prior to a hospital admission for diabetic acidosis. She had been well until thirty-six hours prior to admission, when she had begun to have menstrual cramps accompanied by vomiting as much as ten to fifteen times a day. There was no evidence of infection, she had not neglected to take insulin nor indulged in any dietary irregularities: in short, her attack of diabetic acidosis was unexplained.

At her next menstrual period six weeks later she developed severe abdominal discomfort. The following morning she had increasing abdominal cramps, vomiting, and developed diabetic acidosis. She was again hospitalized and again promptly responded to specific medical treatment. No precipitating cause in terms of specific infection, dietary irregularities, or failure to take insulin was found.

After the second hospitalization she was followed as an outpatient in our Unit. There a more thorough investigation convinced the physician that her dysmenorrhea was related to her vomiting and acidosis. According to her story, she had had moderate dysmenorrhea for several years, and although she had some periods in which she had no discomfort at all (presumably anovulatory ones), whenever she did have cramps, they were severe and associated with nausea and vomiting. She said she had been totally unprepared for her menarche; very frightened by her first period, she had gone to her mother with great anxiety for an explanation. This girl's reaction to menstruation obviously had a considerable emotional component.

After a relatively short period of psychotherapy she experienced much less discomfort with her periods and she ceased to have nausea and vomiting. For the past twelve months she had had no further difficulties either with her menstrual periods or with the control of her diabetes.

This history indicates the importance of considering every patient's physical *and* emotional aspects. Had this girl's emotional response to her menses continued to be unrecognized, it is likely that she would have had repeated attacks of both diabetic acidosis and dysmenorrhea.

Case IV

Another example of the importance of studying and treating the emotional as well as the physical aspects of organic disease is to be found in this patient, a fourteen-year-old boy, who came to us with epilepsy. He had had convulsions early in childhood, but had then had no further difficulty until eight weeks prior to his first visit to our Unit. He was referred to us because of two recent focal seizures of the Jacksonian type. His mother reported that since these seizures her son had been extremely moody and irritable.

In talking to the patient it was evident that he had a multitude of worries. He talked freely about his seizures, and after a short pause in his narrative began to pour out the real causes of the behavior change that his mother had observed. He said the thing that worried him most was that six months previously a friend of his began to have spells and had later been found to have a brain tumor and was at present said to be dying in the hospital. "It sort of makes me wonder whether I might have a tumor, too." He wanted to know what epilepsy was, asked: "Will I die?" and began to cry bitterly. He expressed the fear that he might have one of these spells when he was swimming, and that his seizures would keep him from participating in sports. In addition, he had one of the common concerns of adolescents; he was worried because his adolescent growth spurt had not begun.

An electroencephalogram confirmed the history and findings, and the X-rays of his skull were normal. We were able to reassure him that he did not have a brain tumor. Considerable time was spent explaining to him, in words he could understand, what epilepsy was, why he had these spells and what his future course would be. He was much relieved by this. His worries and moodiness disappeared and his seizure control has been good.

Had this patient been treated without regard for his anxieties, one would have neglected this boy's real problems. It was not that of a focal lesion in one of the hemispheres, but the result of worry concerning a variety of matters and particularly about symptoms which resembled those of his dying friend.

It is at times a problem to get an adolescent to visit a clinic or a physician; even more frequently it is difficult to get him to accept help from a psychiatrist. In a medical clinic we have at our disposal a greater number of maneuvers which serve as reasons for return appointments than in a psychiatric clinic. Patients who are at first reluctant to return often lose their initial resistance after the visits which additional medical or laboratory procedures require; or may be willing to return in order that we may discuss with them the results of the routine laboratory work, or a sore knee, or that we may complete the physical examination. These reasons get them back to us in the instances when they would balk at a return visit "just to talk." The following story illustrates this.

Case V

This sixteen-year-old boy's mother was deeply worried because of his "terrible feelings of depression, his marked inferiority complex, and his inability to get along well with his companions." The boy's parents were divorced, the mother having custody of the children. His elder brother had left college because of a severe emotional disturbance and his younger brother was said to have emotional difficulties.

At his first visit our patient was very suspicious, antagonistic, and extremely defensive. He said he had been told to stay out of sports and to wear a knee bandage. He talked about a variety of symptoms and expressed resentment at his restrictions from athletics. It was clear that he was confused and depressed, and that he had unfortunate personality traits, but he was reluctant to return for any further visits. He denied, although he had been talking a great deal about his various difficulties, that he had any problems, and he refused to return to discuss them. He said he would not see a psychiatrist under any circumstances.

In the hope that on further acquaintance his defensiveness would lessen, he was told that his knee condition was of sufficient importance to warrant attention and observation, and that it would be helped. He was willing to come back on this basis. On the subsequent four or five visits, we ostensibly were concerned only with his mild Osgood-Schlatter's Disease (which, incidentally, had been overtreated), and cautiously helped him to gain a slight amount of insight into his emotional difficulties. After a few visits he accepted a referral to a psychiatrist and is now currently receiving treatment.

In a general practice clinic such as ours various physical aspects of illness as well as laboratory examinations are often used to have a patient return for successive visits in the hope that as a relationship to the physician develops it will later be possible to refer the patient to a specialist. Some who need an expert's help, but who despite our efforts refuse to see a psychiatrist, are willing to come to see a "medical doctor." If this physician has the advantage of a psychiatrist's supervision, as he does in our Unit, he may be able to give the support and treatment which is needed. While none would consider such a recourse ideal, it is obvious that a physician trained in this way should be at least much better for this sort of patient than no treatment at all.

Case VI

This seventeen-year-old girl was referred to us because of psychomotor seizures, recent weight loss, and nervousness. She had had psychomotor seizures since the age of six which had never been well controlled by any medication. Despite superior intelligence she had recently dropped out of school because of her frequent seizures and marked weight loss.

Her weight loss had been accompanied by a "catching feeling" in her midthorax. She said that when she ate she felt as if she had to wash her food down with fluids. She didn't like to eat breakfast, and recently her appetite had decreased sharply. This patient obviously felt her problem was one of insecurity; her seizures made her dread and feel uncertain about her future. She never knew when a seizure would occur, and was unable to plan ahead for dates. She had dysmenorrhea and her menstrual periods which she "hated" were a time of anxiety.

Physical examination showed the early features of cachexia and it was felt that this girl presented an emotional problem which might be considered to be early anorexia nervosa. She was referred to a psychiatrist for treatment, but after several visits decided that she did not want to continue and said that she would prefer to see the physician who had seen her originally. Although it was felt that this arrangement was far from ideal, her request was granted.

Definite progress was made during the year she was seeing this physician. Her dysmenorrhea became less severe, she no longer dreaded her periods, and the severity of her psychomotor seizures decreased. At the end of a year's time, the following statement made us feel that she had improved considerably. "I'm not afraid of men any more, the way I used to be. I can even get along with boys most of the time." Her feelings of inferiority had decreased, and her psychomotor seizures, now quite infrequent, no longer upset her. She no longer feared going out alone, working, or going out on a date. Even though this girl refused a psychiatrist's help, it would appear that all was not lost.

From the foregoing it should be apparent that an adolescent boy or girl is a most satisfactory patient to treat. Whether the illness is organic or emotional in origin or a mixture of the two, the adolescent usually responds to treatment more promptly than do older patients. This rapid and vigorous response to treatment is due to the innate vitality of adolescence and to the emotional state in which most of them function. A state of turbulent excitement is sometimes concealed by an expressionless exterior, but it is there nevertheless, and ready to lend its energy to wholesome action in life. Their turbulence fosters a lively capacity to change. Attitudes, habits, skills, hopes and fears may come or go overnight: the conservatism of early adolescence changes to rebelliousness that sets the older generation (which forgets that it, too, was once rebellious) to shaking its head.

Because the adolescent is close in time to the ways of infancy and childhood to which we all resort when ill, emotional responses to sickness and emotional disorders themselves are apt to develop readily. By the same token, however, these responses and disorders can be modified by proper treatment with relative ease, and we find that two or three visits may suffice to correct them. The internist, general practitioner, or pediatrician, even though limited in the psychiatric assistance he can give a patient, can salvage an adolescent's destiny by his prompt recognition of a problem. He is the person who sees these difficulties early, when they respond most readily.

Another aspect of the adolescent personality which favors prompt response to psychotherapy is its unusual reaction to the treatment relationship. The adolescent who is upset is often so because of his or her failure to make a satisfactory and wholesome identification with his father or her mother. The wholesome ones are hero worshipers and copy mannerisms of an athlete or the style of a favorite teacher. The upset ones are often hungry to find an adult to copy and will readily fasten upon a physician. Once this impulse to copy an adult hero begins to influence the adolescent's behavior, the treatment may be expected to move with gratifying speed. The attraction to the physician which develops in the treatment relationship (technically, the "transference relationship") finds the patient employing old emotional habits which he developed originally in dealing with his parents and siblings. These are now *transferred* to his relationship to his physician. As a consequence, much of the patient's behavior repeats patterns he or she formerly used with parents or siblings and gives the therapist additional knowledge of the way in which his patient's personality developed. Many disturbed adolescents are so because of a failure in the original parent-child relationship: these attach themselves to a physician with a hunger of pathetic intensity. The decision of many adolescents to become doctors may stem from a transference relationship with their physician and their consequent desire to imitate him.

This imitative tendency in adolescents allows simple emotional upsets, even when they occur in a poorly knit personality, to clear up within relatively few visits. The transference relationship can, therefore, be used as a diagnostic and prognostic aid. The adolescent who, though upset, is fundamentally sound will usually establish a strong and persistent transference. On the other hand, if a positive relationship fails to develop or declines, the physician can suspect that he is dealing with a weak personality.

For example, an adolescent patient suffering from early schizophrenia might appear to be much attracted to a therapist only to show after several visits an anger and resentment as intense as the original positive feeling and even more baffling. However, an emotionally disturbed but less seriously ill adolescent who is possessed of a sound personality may appear decidedly diffident at first but will soon develop and maintain a warm and responsive relationship.

An example of a rapid response to a physician's simple psychotherapy is to be found in the case which follows.

Case VII

This fifteen-year-old boy was referred to our Unit because of failure in a college preparatory course. His I.Q. was unusually high. He was doing little or no studying and was considering a change to a trade school. His teachers reported that he daydreamed a great deal, seemed depressed, was envious of others, became angry easily, and had marked feelings of inferiority.

According to his mother, he was $60.00 short on his paper route. Recently a will had been found in which he had bequeathed various items to the family, and it was reported that on being confronted with it he had said, "What's the use of living, we all have to die."

He was quite depressed at his initial visit, did not look at his physician but would look off into space as he talked in a soft voice. However, he talked quite freely about his family, especially about his father and how they didn't get along. He seemed to want to change this, but he felt that he and his father didn't have anything in common. He said that his father didn't have his hobbies, that he just sat and read. "He is highly intellectual—I just can't stand that."

His improvement in four visits was striking. He became

more alert and confident, talked quite freely about his relations at home and at school, and stated that he had decided not to go to trade school.

On his last visit he announced that he had decided not to come in any more, because his classmates were teasing him, saying that he was coming in to see a psychiatrist. He said that he just couldn't stand that, and that he had changed his mind again and was going to go to trade school.

We continued to keep in touch with this boy's progress, although he did not return to the clinic. One year later a report from the high school stated that he had stayed there and that he had made great improvement: he had become quite mature in his thinking and attitude, and was no longer "queer."

Not all cases of emotional disorder in adolescents respond promptly to short-term psychotherapy. This age group has its quota of schizophrenias, anorexia nervosas, and other grave psychopathies that require treatment by specialists. But the preponderance of emotional disturbances, whether alone or concomitant with an organic disease, are amenable to treatment by the pediatrician and internist. Experience with and training in the management of these minor emotional illnesses familiarize the physician with the nature of adolescents' disturbances so that when he meets a more serious mental disorder he is far more likely to recognize it as something that should receive intensive study and treatment than to permit it to go on unrecognized.

It is perhaps hardly necessary to state that we do not consider these young people to have been "cured." We are skeptical of all who use that word. But they apparently have been helped sufficiently so that they can lead effective lives. That goal may seem to some short of desirable, but we would not agree.

Frequently it is necessary to focus on the area of family relationships, for many of the emotional problems that beset these young people arise from them. A domineering mother, a meek and passive father, account for many adolescents' problems.

Case VIII

This fifteen-year-old girl's mother said that she had an underactive thyroid, trouble with her menstrual periods, and nervousness. She had been given thyroid extract two years previously and had continued to take it daily. Her mother also reported that her daughter was nervous and worrisome, that the girls didn't like her, that she didn't "date," and that in spite of high grades she worried about her school work.

At her first visit this girl said that she had dizziness at times at school, especially when she was worried whether she would pass or fail. She also said she had moderately severe cramps and diarrhea on the first day of her menstrual period: "Last period I had to go to bed; I was all doubled up. Sometimes I have to stay out of school. I get so nervous when I have my period."

Her physical examination and laboratory tests failed to reveal any evidence of hypothyroidism; so her thyroid medication was stopped. There was also no evidence of any pelvic disorder. Her symptoms seemed psychosomatic.

She began a series of visits to her physician at the Unit, and during the next six months she was seen once every two weeks. It was clear from the beginning that she was embroiled in a conflict which involved an excessive attachment to her father. Over the weeks her attitudes changed, and she became more feminine. Within three months her symptoms had almost disappeared. She no longer became dizzy, her menstrual cramps were very mild, and she no longer had diarrhea on the first day of her period. She soon began to "date," and at the end of six months said that she felt she no longer needed help.

Similarly, confused by his efforts to be a man like his more fortunate fellows and deprived of a model of many attributes in his father, a boy may try to solve his confusion by refusing to do anything his mother advises in an effort to deny the power of the feminine in himself.

Case IX

This twelve-year-old boy was brought into our Unit because he was stealing money, staying away from home until the early hours of the morning, and being truant from school. His mother said that his behavior had become increasingly rebellious over the past six years. He was the only child of parents who were divorced when he was two and a half years old, and had been brought up by the mother.

At his first visit this boy was extremely rebellious and demanding. He said that the only thing he wanted was a black leather jacket. "That's all I want." He talked about his stealing episodes, said that he just didn't know why he did these things, and spoke with much emotion of his mother's continual nagging and criticism. He talked, too, about his father and ventured the opinion that his father was timid and drank too much. Toward the end of the visit he repeated his wish for a black leather jacket, and said he also wanted to be sixteen years old and to own a car.

As a rule a patient and his mother are seen together at the end of the initial interview. At this one there was a very unpleasant scene in which the patient was rebellious and resentful and made imperious and violent demands on his mother. His allowance wasn't enough; he couldn't go to the movies in town often enough; she wouldn't give him a black leather jacket. "Doctor, why don't you force her to give me a black leather jacket?"

He was subsequently seen several times within a month during which his behavior changed rapidly. He became talkative and friendly, and since his school was nearby, he would often drop into the Unit just to get a drink of water or come in to talk for only a few minutes. He has been seen approximately at monthly intervals for the past year and a half in this unusual fashion. There has been no unacceptable behavior, his school work is excellent, and the report from his summer camp was extremely complimentary.

SUMMARY

The Adolescent Unit of the Children's Medical Center and the manner in which its physicians and its psychiatric consultants work together are described. Brief case reports illustrate both the psychotherapeutic methods used and also some of the characteristics of adolescents' emotional difficulties which make those methods appropriate for use in this age group.

The practice of psychotherapy by those general practitioners, internist, and pediatricians who deal with adolescents is desirable because of the large number of adolescents who have minor but significant emotional problems.

Adolescents' somatic symptoms will be more accurately diagnosed when emotional components are always given consideration.

The objection that many adolescents have to going to a psychiatrist is overcome by having them seen by physicians who under training and supervision can handle transference relationships and either the adolescents themselves, or if a specialist's treatment is needed, effect a transition to a psychiatrist.

The proper treatment of emotional disorders in adolescence is an effective preventive against the development of such disorders in the adult. When adolescents' disorders are recognized and properly treated early in their course, they are likely to respond rapidly, and can be prevented from becoming chronic and resistant to treatment. It is the family doctor, the pediatrician, and the internist who are most likely to see these young people early: it is they who must be skillful in understanding adolescents if preventive measures are to become more widespread.

6

PSYCHOTHERAPY OF ADOLESCENTS AT INTENSIVE HOSPITAL TREATMENT LEVEL

DONALD C. GREAVES, M.D.
and
PETER F. REGAN, III, M.D.

In our experience, only a small minority of patients under twenty years of age need psychotherapy in a hospital setting. When admission to a hospital is necessary, however, the problem is a more complicated one than would arise with the admission of an adult patient. The hospital must provide an environment which at the same time protects the patient, promotes his return to health, and allows him to continue his maturation in social, educational, and physical spheres.

In this presentation, we shall give a picture of the various methods which have been used at the Payne Whitney Psychiatric Clinic, with their advantages and disadvantages as we see them. These methods work satisfactorily at present, and we have been able to increase the percentage of patient days devoted to the treatment of adolescents from 8 per cent in 1944 to 17 per cent in 1954. The present average length of stay per patient is seven months. The methods are, however, in a state of flux, as new knowledge causes modification of our previous ideas. Because the environment itself becomes an important part of the treatment plan, a brief description of the structure and treatment of the hospital seems warranted.

TREATMENT SETTING

The Payne Whitney Psychiatric Clinic is a 108-bed psychiatric hospital, divided into five units of about twenty patients each. These units differ from each other in terms of restrictions, nursing staff, and therapeutic facilities. On one extreme, for example, adequate protection and care can be given to patients with active suicidal tendencies, assaultiveness, excitements and antisocial behavior difficulties. Suicidal precautions are in full force. The ratio of staff to patients is high and the patients are expected to assume only those responsibilities which they can bear. At the other extreme, the doors are unlocked, patients care for their own rooms, and staffing needs are minimal. All patients are out of the clinic for exercise and air for at least one hour a day; and many patients leave the clinic daily to attend work, school or housekeeping responsibilities. In many respects it is like a well-organized club.

Throughout the five floors the social setting is consistent. On all floors there are both men and women of all ages and diagnostic categories. Scheduled activities in occupational and recreational therapy fill six to eight hours per day. No distinction is made among patients on a socioeconomic basis; and restraints and seclusion are never used.

Patients are selected for admission from voluntary applicants in accordance with therapeutic, investigative and teaching needs. Adolescent patients are admitted either because of an acute illness of emergency nature or because their illness is such that they can no longer function effectively in the home, community or school. Most of these patients have had a trial at ambulatory psychotherapy before application for admission is made. They encompass all diagnostic categories. Schizophrenic reactions are common, but there is a large proportion of psychoneuroses of various types, psychophysiological disorders, and psychopathic or character disorders.

GENERAL PRINCIPLES OF THERAPY

Intensive dynamic psychotherapy is the keystone of treatment at the hospital. A crucial part of this psychotherapy is the frequent long-term contact betwen an individual patient and his physician, through which the patient seeks relief of symptoms with expansion and growth of personality. As in any therapeutic management, the technique employed by the physician must depend on the goals set for the patient, and these goals may be shifted or modified in the course of treatment, thus necessitating a change in technique. Therapy always involves the recognition of transference, resistance, and unconscious dynamic material, regardless of how the physician employs these concepts.

When the patient is admitted to the hospital, the psychotherapeutic program necessarily extends throughout the twenty-four hours, a condition drastically different from treatment in the private office. The availability of five units, with their wide range of socially acceptable behavior, allows us to carry on such therapy within a framework which enables each patient to live in a therapeutic milieu which is as close to his normal life as his capabilities permit. Thus, a patient who is severely disturbed at the time of admission will be admitted to a closed floor where he will be guided, protected, and encouraged. As he recovers, he will gradually move to less and less restricted floors, assuming increasing responsibilities with each move. Such transfers are common, and are guided by the psychopathologic state of the patient. These moves enable the patient to live constantly as an accepted member of the group; his self-respect and individuality can be maintained, he assumes as much responsibility as he is able and the over-all setting is as close to his everyday life as is possible.

The knowledge derived from therapeutic interviews can be used to modify the environmental pattern, where necessary, in the individual case; extra nursing attention, special diets, sleeping or eating arrangements and tutoring are only a few of the ways in which this can be done. If therapy is being retarded because the social demands of one floor are too great for the patient to handle while he discusses dynamic material, he might be moved to a more protected floor until the disturbing problems are brought under control. Or, if it seem therapeutically wiser to let the patient remain in a situation he is not handling well, he may be helped to analyze the meaning and effects of his acting out.

TREATMENT OF THE ADOLESCENT

The policies which have been given indicate how the structure of the hospital environment can be used as well as modified and manipulated where any patient's therapeutic needs warrant it. The interdependence of environment and individual psychotherapeutic interviews is even more important when applied to the adolescent patient. For convenience in illustration, these two concepts are discussed separately.

Environment

The need to provide a realistic and healthy social environment for adolescents has influenced the policy with regard to their location and distribution in the hospital. The adolescent needs adequate relationships with both peers and adults. He is in a period of active psychobiological growth where formal education, sexual maturation, habit training, and changing awareness of himself must be considered. To place him on a unit devoted exclusively to his age group and sex would simplify some aspects of his care, but it would deprive him of some opportunities to learn and grow. Because most of our adolescents stay in the hospital for six to twelve months, we are reluctant to deprive them of these opportunities. It was therefore arranged for adolescent patients to live in the same units with both men and women of all ages, and in about the same ratio as may be found in normal life.

This policy of even distribution results in a relatively stable number of adolescent patients in the hospital. Attention must also be given to assigning adolescents to the different patient units. We have found that one or two adolescents in a twenty-patient unit became isolated, anxious, and withdrawn. On the other hand, if more than six or seven adolescents are present in a unit at one time, group living for the adults may become impossible. On one occasion when this occurred, the piano and television set on one floor were dismantled, the corridor was used as a bowling alley, and only by transferring some adolescent patients could social order be restored. Usually four or five adolescent patients in a twenty-patient unit will provide satisfactory and nondisruptive group relationships.

Intermingling of sexes and ages sometimes creates problems which the therapist must guard against. For example, some adult patients identify strongly with the adolescent group. Frequently they are "leaders" and stimulate group rebellion or destructiveness. Socially, they are "adolescent," and must be managed as such. "Sibling" rivalry may also become troublesome when one therapist is treating more than one adolescent patient on a single unit. Adult patients may stimulate or encourage transference reactions in adolescents with the gamut of neurotic problems that this implies: dependence, rebellion, or sexual seduction. On the whole, however, these difficulties can be kept within reasonable limits and turned to therapeutic usefulness, if the individual therapist and the psychiatrist in charge of administration are both aware of the situation.

It is clear that the mixture of men and women, boys and girls, is useful in providing areas for discussion in interviews. For instance, it affords the adolescent a chance to work out some of the problems involved in sexual maturation. However, the adolescent must be adequately protected from undesirable sexual activity with other adolescents, from excessive mastubatory or fantasy experience, and from seduction by adult men or women patients. An adolescent may develop a heterosexual or homosexual crush on another adolescent or adult patient. As long as overt manifestations of this are controlled, and as long as the therapist sees no danger signs in interviews, these experiences are allowed to follow their natural course. If the situation becomes a dangerous one, however, the relationship must be terminated. The method of such a termination must be determined in accordance with psychotherapeutic needs and the dynamics of the relationships. It may be done by interview discussions, by administrative prohibition, or by administrative transfer of one of the patients to another unit in the hospital. In sexual matters, particularly, standards of social acceptability must be the basis of any action on the part of the therapist or hospital.

Schooling is a necessity when the adolescent is hospitalized over many months. Provided there is no psychotherapeutic obstacle, tutoring is begun as a substitute for other scheduled hospital activities as soon as the patient is ready for it. Sometimes a tutor begins working with a catatonic patient only a few days after the patient has begun to talk. The schooling process proceeds during the entire hospitalization with variations in the instruction plan or content according to the changing needs of the patient. When patients are able to visit out of the hospital, resumption of full-time school is arranged in appropriate public or private schools in New York City. In this connection the therapist must function *in loco parentis* and make certain that the patient has adequate room and time for doing his assignments.

It should be emphasized that the patient's family must be brought into the treatment situation. A detailed investigation of the family constellation, social, cultural, economic and ethnic factors will give the best leads as to how they may be most effectively motivated and encouraged to participate. It is a frequent tendency of psychiatrists, and of young psychiatrists in particular, to side with the patient in his adolescent struggles with his parents. This will result in an increase of the parents' hostility, anxiety and guilt, thereby working against the patient's ultimate benefit.

The preliminary inquiry into the family past and present is best carried out by the therapist who is treating the child. Only after such a study can the therapist decide such questions as: Do the parents require treatment, and if so, by whom? Would a social worker be of help in more detailed inquiry? Should the parents be asked to curtail visiting? We feel that all these matters must be decided, not arbitrarily, but according to individual needs. For example, one may ask overanxious or overprotective parents not to visit their child until a good relationship has been established with the physician. Some parents may be encouraged to visit early and often if this will help the child adjust more easily to confinement in what may be a bewildering and frightening place for him. A thorough understanding of the pathology and dynamics of each case will guide the therapist in these decisions.

In addition to these major areas, a number of less striking but equally important problems must be handled. The adolescent's physical and social development must be supported with exercise and instruction in athletics, and sufficient unstructured social interchange.

Furthermore, what shall the adolescent be called? It is true that essential warmth, friendliness and respect may be conveyed by the individual therapist without regard to the title assigned the adolescent, but he must be called something by the hospital staff and other patients. It is our belief that the young patient striving for maturity and adult prerogatives responds well to being treated, and addressed, as are the adult patients with whom he is living; therefore our present policy is to call patients sixteen years of age or younger by their first name, and those seventeen or older by their last name. This is based on the premise that it is as unwise to call a thirteen-year-old, "Miss," as to call an immature thirty-year-old, "Mary."

The families' policies are followed with regard to allowing smoking, the use of stimulants, clothing, personal hygiene and manners, provided these seem within normal cultural limits. The provision of an allowance adequate to meet current needs is recommended. It appears important to us that deviations in these fields be discussed frankly, but not rigidly, with patients.

It should be emphasized again that these over-all policies have been established to provide a basic framework, and to organize a therapeutic milieu which will be healthy for all patients, adults and adolescents alike. Flexibility is essential if the milieu is also to be therapeutic for each patient.

Interview Psychotherapy

Most of the problems occurring within the therapeutic interview are the same, whether the patient be in or out of a hospital; as such, they are beyond the scope of this paper. Where adolescents are treated in a hospital, the authors believe that some psychotherapists are personally better equipped to provide optimal treatment. In addition to those qualities needed in any psychotherapy, the psychiatrist needs to have a large fund of warmth, patience, and intuitive spontaneity. He must be prepared to assume a variety of roles, and to shift rapidly and confidently from role to role. He will need to function, at various times, as parent, protector, teacher, sympathizer, and friend to his patient. It should be emphasized that this does not mean only that he appears to function in these ways, or that these are only transference phenomena; in addition to such appearances, he must actually function in these capacities when the need arises. To do so while avoiding the distortions of counter-transference and maintaining psychotherapeutic progress is sometimes difficult.

In order to aid in this task, many procedures have been utilized. The Psychiatrist-in-Chief and another senior staff member each spend three supervisory hours per week with every therapist, seeing his patients, and aiding in the under-standing of pathology, dynamics and therapeutic relationships. In daily conferences, the entire staff, nursing supervisors, and recreational and occupational therapists review the status of the patient from a comprehensive viewpoint. Also, a child psychiatrist meets with each physician treating an adolescent patient at least once a month.

In addition to the above procedures, the administration is so structured as to forestall the undesirable consequences that might arise if the therapist should assume an admin-istrative role. Thus, over-all administration is in the hands of a physician who does not treat patients in the hospital, and each unit is under the administrative charge of a specific physician. The degree to which administrative functions are borne by the individual therapist will vary from patient to patient. Occasionally, differences in viewpoint arise between therapist and administrator. It is important that such dif-ferences be readily brought into awareness and resolved by whatever means necessary, especially since countertransfer-ence distortions are often the basis of dissent.

Within this system of checks and balances, there are cer-tain assets and liabilities which accrue in the hospital treat-ment of the adolescent. The actual admission of the patient produces some of these. With fearful, bewildered patients desperately trying to control themselves, admission to a secure environment, where they are protected and respected, will frequently allow for an easing of pressure, and the establishment of a therapeutic relationship proceeds rapidly and securely. On the other hand, anxiety may be provoked by admission, and may show itself, especially in the adolescent, by sullenness, withdrawal, rebelliousness, or negativism. These difficulties can then only be overcome by patience and skill; at the very least, with the patient in the hospital, the therapist can be sure of frequent contact.

An unavoidable aspect of most hospitals, and especially teaching hospitals, is that changes in staff occur regularly, and it may be necessary for the patient to change therapists during his hospitalization. Occasionally, a change in therapists is valuable, and the therapeutic progress is improved. Usually, the continuity of supervision and environmental policies allow the change to take place with minimal difficulty. Experience has shown that poor results occasionally develop. These were usually seen when a suitable therapist for the patient was not available or when the selection of the new therapist was poorly advised; infrequently, management of the transfer by one of the therapists has been a contributory factor.

The hospital's authority, furthermore, will stir up anxiety, hostility, or rebelliousness at one time or another in most adolescents.

One seventeen-year-old boy, after running away from school and acting as a vagrant, attempted suicide and was admitted to the hospital. Here, he refused to follow the routine, to have anything to do with other patients, or to talk in interviews. After several weeks of contact with his therapist, during which the similarity of the patient's and therapist's goals were emphasized again and again, he began to talk in interview, and the rebelliousnes disappeared. As therapy continued, sporadic recurrences of rebellion were evident whenever the patient felt any doubts about his therapist.

Thus, it has appeared to us that the wisest course is for the therapist to accept the existence of this authority, and of his share of it, in a realistic way. He can then strive to clarify for the adolescent patient the fact that authority is unavoidable, and that he is the patient's partner in organizing the most healthy ways of dealing with the authority. To do this effectively the therapist must have satisfactorily worked through his own attitudes toward authority.

The chief advantages offered by the hospital to the interview psychotherapy are those of observation and security. In the hospital setting, the therapist sees the patient every day. He is aware of the patient's care of his room, of his dealings with staff and other patients. He knows the characteristics of the persons whom the patient likes and dislikes, and has the benefit of objective reporting of the methods by which the patient relates to people. This information can then be used to help the patient analyze current relationships, to interpret transference, and to illustrate unconscious content. Intellectualization and other mechanisms of resistance can be brought to analysis rapidly. When the patient is aware that acting out has been observed and reported, he is spared the ever-difficult task of confessing this to his therapist.

The security of the hospital, like the facility of observation, will occasionally cause resentment in the patient. Its benefits, however, are clear. The patient lives in whatever degree of social reality he can effectively deal with in his current psychopathologic state. Thus, both the therapist and the patient may proceed with confidence in an analysis of material such as homicidal transference feelings, knowing that the patient's anxiety will not have disastrous consequences in the social situation, and that the environment will prevent the full acting out of the impulses.

This is illustrated in the case of a thirteen-year-old boy who was admitted to the hospital after a series of incidents in which he had destroyed furniture in his home and used the threat of violence to force his mother to sleep with him.

Following admission, he made a good adjustment, established a firm relationship with his therapist and was transferred to a convalescent floor. As infantile incestuous fantasies came to analysis, progress became slow as the patient expressed increasing hostility to the therapist. Finally, the aggression was acted out in the interview situation in several homicidal assaults on the therapist. The latter was able to control these without undue anxiety because of superior physical strength and the knowledge of readily available help. With the recognition that the therapist would not allow him to commit homicide, and would remain warm toward him despite the desire, the patient was able to work through the sexual involvement with his mother in a satisfactory fashion.

Frequently, however, patients are not able to discuss sensitive material on convalescent floors. Only by a temporary transfer to a floor with a larger nursing staff and more security can such material then be analyzed.

A seventeen-year-old boy was admitted to a convalescent floor because of repeated failures in school attributed to emotional difficulties. He had not responded to a trial at outpatient psychotherapy. In the hospital, as in previous therapy, he was unproductive, sullen, denied the existence of illness, and was hostile to his therapist. This pattern continued for two months, during which time his behavior was satisfactory and he was allowed to visit out of the clinic. Finally, however, he was transferred to a restricted floor, was not permitted to receive visitors or leave the clinic. Within ten days, he could admit the severity of his illness and his difficulty in expressing his conflicts. He pleaded for help and entered into a good therapeutic relationship.

Conversely, when a patient is admitted to a restricted floor it may be difficult to gauge the severity of psychopathology or gain a dynamic understanding until he is transferred to an open unit where more is expected of him.

This may be demonstrated by a case where chronic anxiety, tension, depression, social withdrawal, and preoccupation with homosexual fantasies led to the admission of an eighteen-year-old boy. Initially, therapy progressed satisfactorily, but interviews became unproductive when the patient was transferred to a convalescent floor, where his behavior became increasingly listless, apathetic, and sloppy. The behavioral difficulties forced a transfer back to a restricted floor where a week was devoted to analysis of his behavior on the open floor. He was then able to express his hostility toward his therapist, which he had previously manifested only indirectly in appearance and social behavior. He secured steady employment at the end of the week, and therapy proceeded effectively thereafter.

CRITERIA FOR DISCHARGING ADOLESCENT PATIENTS

The social reality afforded by the hospital, however elaborate the program may be, can provide only a substitute for the patient's genuine environmental reality. Awareness of this fact influences our policy of having the patients resume school and family contacts outside the hospital as soon as possible. It also influences our discharge of patients from the hospital. As soon as the patient has made sufficient progress in psychotherapy so that he can make a good adaptation to a more realistic environment, his discharge is arranged. Under varying conditions, this discharge may be to his home, to a foster home, to a boarding school, or to one of the schools equipped to provide a good environment for children with mild emotional difficulties. In all cases a suitable means of continuation of psychotherapy must be insured.

SUMMARY

The number of adolescents who require psychiatric hospitalization is relatively small, but looms large when the available facilities are considered. The authors have attempted to demonstrate the complexity of the social, biological, educational, administrative, and therapeutic problems which must be met in the process of providing these facilities. The methods which have evolved at the Payne Whitney Psychiatric Clinic between 1944 and 1954, in the treatment of 225 adolescent patients, have been described. These methods have provided a workable basis for psychotherapy in the setting of a general psychiatric hospital. If there is any keynote in these methods, it is that of flexibility based on a keen awareness of the complexity of the problem.

7

DISCUSSION OF PRECEDING CHAPTERS

I. Discussion of Chapters I, II, III

EXIE E. WELSCH, M.D.

The areas of basic agreement in these papers are remarkably numerous even though different settings and somewhat different theoretical frames of references are presented by the three authors. These areas of agreement would seem to point to certain fundamental common denominators which may possibly comprise a working base for therapy with adolescents regardless of the particular theoretical base from which the individual therapist worked.

Basic agreement seemed to be in the following areas: (1) that extraordinary flexibility of approach is required on the part of the therapist treating an adolescent; (2) that orthodoxy of technique, of whatever specific type, is rarely usable in toto in the treatment of adolescents; (3) that analysis of the psychodynamics of the adolescent's biographical past is rarely appropriate or successful in treatment of adolescents although unresolved problems of childhood are to be seen by the therapist as contributing to the turbulence of adolescence and weakening his adaptive capacities during that period; (4) that supporting and strengthening of ego function is most appropriate in therapy with adolescents; (5) that the adolescent most frequently utilizes the therapeutic approach related to his current and immediate concerns; (6) that adolescents are exceptionally labile emotionally and therapy is directed toward helping the adolescent develop objectivity and more stable and mature value judgments about his own behavior in relation to present reality situations; (7) that the changes accompanying sexual maturation offer new realities with which the adolescent has to cope; (8) that treatment of adolescents differs in technical approach from that of children or of adults but utilizes some of the techniques of each; (9) that treatment of the adolescent is usually shorter in duration (than that of psychoanalysis of adults); (10) that parents exist and require attention to varying degrees in the interest of successful pursuit of therapy for the adolescent; (11) that the adolescent's need for and view of the therapist as a helping person has unique qualities and the therapist needs to be sensitive to the role and meaning he or she has for the adolescent in order to avoid certain pitfalls and at the same time to represent a stable, empathetic maturity which offers opportunity for the adolescent's own reality testing; (12) that regardless of the specific techniques used and the immediate urgency dealt with by the adolescent, a full dynamic understanding of the adolescent's physical status, personality structure, and adaptive patterns is required on the part of the therapist.

Some of the differences which also seem basic stem from the different theoretical approaches of the authors. Dr. Josselyn, for instance, sees the adolescent as a psychological entity whose overtaxed ego is battling with primary internal struggles from which the problems of adaptation to the external world results. Dr. Robinson sees the adolescent as an individual pursuing his growth toward individuation but in a context predicated on the belief that growth and maturation evolve from the mutual interaction of parent and child. Whereas one sees the adolescent primarily as impinging himself upon the world and reacting to it in turn, the other sees the adolescent primarily as being what he or she is, in terms of efforts at working out a more mature and appropriate emotional relationship with parents.

This leads to certain differences in therapeutic procedures as they relate to goals of therapy. Whereas both have a deep and genuine regard for the adolescent as an individual (which is probably basic and an important factor as to why each is so successful in treating this age group), Dr. Josselyn in the section on role of parents in therapy sees the essence of therapy as that which accrues from the doctor-patient relationship. The parents' attitude toward their children's therapy is determined, but essentially only to prevent their impeding treatment. Dr. Peltz commented on the need for conferences with parents of children in difficulties in school. He did not etch out in detail the purpose and goals of such contacts, but one gained the impression that the role of the psychiatrist with the parents was primarily an advisory one. Dr. Robinson's view is that active participation of the parent is essential in treatment (at the level and pace that the parent has the capacity for) toward increased and more satisfactory communication between adolescent and parent at a level congruent with the healthy needs of each.

Some psychiatrists have found it therapeutically useful to include the parents at some level of activity and participation (as both Dr. Josselyn and Dr. Robinson do in reality, in accordance with their own objectives) with a view toward helping them acquire a more realistic and satisfying relationship with their maturing offspring. The degree of participation will undoubtedly be affected by the accessibility of the parents and be more easily gained when the adolescent lives at home than when he or she is away at boarding school or in psychiatric residence.

This particular emphasis on help to the parents, which in turn will help the adolescent, is not stated in Dr. Josselyn's paper and, though not stated as explicitly, is implicit in Dr. Robinson's way of working. Sometimes it is essential to help the parent seek therapy for himself, a possibility which Dr. Josselyn includes.

Another difference can be found in successful therapeutic procedures for the adolescent as contrasted to methods of analysis for adults. Dr. Josselyn anticipates criticisms that such treatment may not be considered "analysis," is merely "relationship" or "common sense" therapy or scarcely within the realm of warranting the dignity of being called professional effort. She goes ahead to say that the success of therapy (with adolescents) is often "inexplicable" or "unorthodox."

Dr. Robinson did not reveal such concern, at least he doesn't mention it.

The presence and the absence of concern on this point in these two papers was interesting. It would seem to be related to the difference in basic theory, the difference in the initial frame of reference from which each departs in order to explore the special and unique aspects of adolescence. Psychoanalysis, beginning historically from work with adult neurotics, views patients of all ages essentially in terms of a personality structure that was in the main established in childhood. Therefore, it uses techniques of therapy designed to modify that personality structure rather than specific symptoms. A certain investment occurs in this form and approach. Thus arises the problem of criticism, defensiveness or apology for deviations in concept or approach. This would seem to be the basis for the intellectual concern of Dr. Josselyn. Dr. Robinson's methods emerge, with alterations, from psychiatric concepts arising from outpatient child guidance practice, which historically began with the focus on the child. This focus led to study concerning the nature of growth and development of the personality from infancy to adulthood, to observations concerning the essential dependency of childhood upon parental care and scrutiny of factors both within the child and external to him which reciprocally influence growth. This view enables Dr. Robinson not only to see adolescence as a special period in growth but also to view it as part of the whole longitudinal process of growth toward maturity. Thus he states specifically that "treatment of an adolescent [is] an active process directed toward what he is able to become," and utilizes the parents as part of the process. An example of the impact of these differing theoretical concepts upon concepts of therapy is seen in Dr. Peltz's statement that treatment with children is "education" while treatment with adults is directed toward developing "insight," and that modifications of each may need to be used in treatment of the adolescent. Dr. Robinson is perhaps not troubled because his own frame of reference sees treatment as comprised of a vital ongoing process of change and maturation at all levels and stages of development (as contrasted to "education" and "insight" per se) with continuity from one to the other. This is in contrast to the more compartmentalized "education"—"insight" view.

In her case reports, Dr. Josselyn surmounts the theoretical questions she poses. Clinically, she has experimented with "more orthodox" methods of therapy and found them wanting or even catastrophic (except with the full-blown neuroses which seem to fit more the pattern of adult psychoanalytic practice) and has boldly set down her clinically tested observations, including some very valuable ones as to the meaning the adolescent's therapy may have for parents. Especially welcome is her implied caution (to therapists) not to equate anxious parents necessarily as *a priori* "meddling" or "rejecting" parents.

It is helpful, however, to discuss the differences in treatment techniques used for adults and children. Such a discussion underlines the fact that therapy of adolescents demands a different set of approaches and principles for those who on the one hand may tend to offer treatment to adolescents based on the concept that they are immature or embryonic adults, or who on the other hand may approach them as overgrown children. The authors agree that clinically treatment of adolescents differs in technical approach from that of other ages. It would be helpful to the field of general psychiatry if this could be followed up with a thoughtful delineation of the training required to fulfill this area of need in the therapeutic armamentarium. Too often training in child psychiatry stops short of intensive study of this age group and adult psychiatry tends to begin with those at the level of young adults who have already passed through their adolescent years.

There are some areas of consideration which are omitted in these three presentations but which have some importance and perhaps basic significance in the lives of adolescents and affect their problems of maturation and adaptation toward a happy, useful, and creative adulthood. These have to do primarily with areas of reality which impinge upon the adolescent and create areas of conflict between ideals set up by family and our own historical past and those situations which threaten or limit attainment of these ideals. What is unprovoking to an adolescent of one culture may cause problems for an adolescent reared in another culture. The frequency of troubled adolescence in our culture needs to be seen as a reflection of the complexity of problems posed from the outside. For instance, there are general tensions of the times with unwholesomeness and uncertainty from many sources such as increase in prejudices, fear, suspicion, and conflicting moral values of the present era; criticism of independent thought and pressures toward conformity; disruption of plans for normal peacetime goals in anticipation of possible military service and uncertainties as to the future; reality, educational, and vocational problems in relation to the future (as suggested in Dr. Peltz's paper); and lacks in wholesome recreational opportunity.

There is a general lack of status for adolescents and children in our culture, as seen in the perennial difficulty of providing adequate educational and vocational opportunities for them and uncertainty as to employment which is appropriately satisfying. The economic and social pressures felt by parents and adults generally are also reflected in the goals of life of the adolescent and his peer group as seen in their wish to "live it up," to make money, to become powerful at almost any expense. This is in contrast to the more accepted social goals of inner and outer tranquility for the individual, a richness derived from warm, cherished personal relationships, and values pegged on respect for the individual as he contributes according to his own capacity to the lives of those about him and to the community.

Although physiological and sexual maturation problems per se were mentioned, to this should be added the adolescent's attitudes toward his own body, weight, height, and such physiological and biological realities that can be troublesome. Adolescents' view of themselves also stem from their state of good or bad health or from chronic physical limitations, and importantly affect their view of themselves as adequately masculine or feminine figures. The "norm" they gauge themselves by is determined by peers, family patterns of physical structure, and standards as set forth by movies, comics, or other current literature. Current patterns of dating and sexual behavior of adults and in the peer group are significant. Changes in such cultural factors from one period to another determine the areas which do or do not become conflictual for the adolescent.

The marked difference in views regarding the role of parents in relation to their adolescent's therapy may well stem from the fact that we have not given the careful observation, thoughtfulness and analysis to the role of parents and adolescents that has been worked out in regard to parents and the younger child.

These comments on the common denominators, differences, as well as on some of the omissions are made in an attempt at integrating these stimulating presentations.

Especially impressive was the excellently clear and objective evaluation of the role of the therapist in Dr. Josselyn's paper and her suggestions regarding handling of acting-out behavior as well as her description of the use of a dynamic understanding of adolescence and the technical approaches required for successful therapy.

Dr. Peltz's paper underscored the principles that psychiatric consultation in schools requires that psychiatrists be dynamically oriented and be aware of the complicating potential of the dual role as school consultant and therapist as it may impinge upon the adolescent. He points out, furthermore, the need for the psychiatrist to learn about and become oriented to the philosophy and pedagogical goals of education.

Some of the complicated problems with parents presented by Dr. Peltz point again to the need for extending help to parents. Such help may appropriately be therapy, as observed by Dr. Josselyn and others. When such referrals have "results [that] are all too often unsatisfactory," it is possible that casework help with the parent in conjunction with psychiatric therapy for the adolescent may be the method of choice. The role of the caseworker in such settings is currently being given special emphasis in some schools of social work.

Dr. Robinson gave us a clear analysis of the specific use and values of the residence setting for psychotherapy of adolescents and the corollary help to parents. Basing his approach on his experience with the child guidance and child psychiatric viewpoints, he regards the adolescent in the context of his total growth process from infancy to maturity. Differentials from adult perspectives are apparently of little concern to him since he has a basic concept of life constituting a dynamic growth process through various stages from infancy to adulthood, in which the various phases represent part of the maturation process. As a corollary of this, his expectations toward the parents' participation is also different.

Dr. Robinson considers the choice of residence treatment as primarily the prerogative of the parent, which underscores his concept of the nature of parental responsibility. Although such decision is primarily a parental responsibility, the child also should participate in the considerations of its advisability. The psychiatrist also has an important role in determining the psychiatric indications for residential treatment as contrasted to other kinds of psychiatric care. Moreover, it is his responsibility to convey his recommendations to both parents and adolescent in such a way that they can accept and benefit from them.

II. Discussion of Chapters IV, V, VI

ELEANOR A. STEELE, M.D.

In discussing these interesting presentations which emphasize such important issues in the treatment of adolescents in three different settings, I am inclined to concentrate on certain essential similarities which these authors all agree are basic in our understanding and approach to the adolescent and his problems.

In these three chapters it was gratifying to note that there was agreement upon the principle that therapeutic work with the adolescent should be based on a dynamic understanding of the unconscious conflicts and childhood patterns which disturb the development and adjustment of the adolescent to present reality.

Secondly it was generally agreed that the basic threpeutic objective in this age group should be directed toward "strengthening the ego," and, as Dr. Berman said, "the therapist should not become involved in the infantile and childhood conflict"—except, I would amend, from the level of ego interpretation of these conflicts, which will have the helpful strengthening effect which is so necessary to the adolescent.

The third point of important agreement emphasized the attitude of the therapist, both in relation to unconscious countertransference reactions as well as his conscious presentation of himself.

That these important considerations are uniformly emphasized by authors writing from such different theaters of operation, and necessarily dealing with adolescents of varying degrees of maladjustment, lends validity to and stresses the importance of these general principles in the work with the adolescent. Also, it is particularly interesting to find that basic principles which psychiatrists and psychoanalysts agree upon can be utilized at the clinic and hospital level by physicians not primarily trained in psychiatry. It is very important for all of us to know that in dealing with the adolescent's problems, these physicians, in cooperation with psychiatric guidance, can produce such effective results. Our theories in psychiatry are best validated by their workability, and the report from the Boston group verified to some additional extent the workability or practicality of these basic therapeutic principles.

In the past five to ten years particularly, there has been increasing emphasis accorded to the psychiatrist's countertransference reactions toward his patient, and this emphasis is apparent in the preceding chapters. Dr. Berman, Dr. Harris and Dr. Heald all stress the importance of the therapist's resolution of his own anxiety conflicts. The adolescent requires an optimum mixture of secure humility in his therapist and is unusually sensitive to subtle insecurities and defensive maneuvers in the therapeutic situation. Dr. Berman wisely discusses the detrimental effects on the adolescent of an anxiety-laden therapeutic relationship that might arise when the therapist's own adolescent difficulties and blind spots are consciosuly or unconsciously reactivated by the therapeutic situation. Though these countertransference problems are of importance in any kind of therapy, they are particularly important in the management of adolescents. Perhaps more than any other group of patients, adolescents are particularly sensitive to nuances of feeling and attitude in a therapist.

Closely allied with the question of the success of therapy, and with the attitude of the therapist toward the adolescent, is the basic psychological, even biological fact that adolescents are eager to emancipate themselves from the past and from parents by attachment to parent substitutes. This eagerness for growth and emancipation, however hampered by fixations in the adolescent's character make-up, offers a particular opportunity to the outsider who is able to ally himself with this potentiality of the adolescent. The therapist who is interested in giving the adolescent what he wants and needs at this time can further the normal emancipation need of the young person. This is certainly "after-education." For the disturbed youngster this role should be available in the therapist, if his attitudes and skills are sensitively geared to the specific needs of the individual adolescent.

Two divergent generalizations have been expressed in these papers: (1) "that the adolescent does not quickly become engaged in therapy on a collaborative basis," and (2) "that he is a most satisfactory patient to therapists." This divergence in opinion may be due to the therapist's lack of focus on some specific need of the adolescent patient. If the therapist does not understand and ally himself with these specific needs of the adolescent, he can hardly expect collaboration from a young person who is eager to find ways and means of getting these needs satisfied. The problem of the "constructive" versus the "destructive" ways of obtaining satisfaction becomes a secondary problem of development once rapport is adequately established.

Although generalizations are difficult to make, most disturbed adolescents are eager for help, and are very ready to use it when it is geared to what they need and not geared to what the adult feels the adolescent "should want" or "should have" at this time. This reiterates again that the therapist must be singularly free of emancipation problems of his own, and quite willing to go along with what may seem to him, from a reality or long-term point of view, an irrelevant need at the time of therapy. The willingness of the therapist to lend himself to the adolescent along the adolescent's line of direction offers a basic, trusting confidence from an adult to a young person which has value far beyond the content of the interest itself. For instance, the adolescent's need to feel that his own interests and ideas, concerns and thoughts, are of some basic worth and importance is translated by him into the basic feeling: "I am of worth and importance." This need is easily supported by the sympathetic therapist who is less concerned with the content of the interest per se than with the adolescent's right to have his own interests and to develop them along the lines that he sees fit. This vote of confidence from therapist to adolescent is often unrelated to the demands and requirements of the parents or of a given authority. However, it goes without saying that such a vote of confidence must be governed by common sense, constructive boundaries which offset destructive and masochistic impulses in the adolescent.

The Scylla and Charybdis of the dependency-independency conflict in the adolescent is well known. While he needs and demands freedom in many areas, there is a counter-pull toward regressed and excessive submission to authority. This problem is often a dominant one and frequently reflects the parents' failure to recognize and encourage the adolescents' "need to know" and his right to growth and development toward independence. Therapists too may lack this basic sympathy with the adolescents' "need to know"; they may depreciate his interests, his sexuality; and, like parents, therapists may be either consciously or unconsciously too critical of the individual deviations and variations they find in the adolescents' attitudes. In another extreme, too, we find large numbers of adolescents who need to have in the therapist an authoritative person who will safeguard them from rejection, and who will stand firm and help them control their antisocial or masochistic impulses. The sensitive understanding on all levels which is required of the therapist for the adolescent is very great. But in addition (as has been emphasized over and over again in these papers), the therapist must use his skills and understanding to establish a common-sense, "ego-building" rapport which fills the specific needs and corrects the specific blunders of the adolescents' past. Each adolescent, as Thomas Payne says of everyone, "must take his freedom," but how he is best helped to do so in a constructive way can be both difficult and easy, depending on the adolescent and the therapist's skill and understanding.

There is one specific fact which helps the therapist with his own prejudices and partially unresolved adolescent impulses. It is the fact that we all feel that the struggles of adolescents are more or less "normal." Although adolescents, like adults, are striving for freedom from the crippling domination of attitudes and patterns carried over from childhood, in the adolescent there is less judgmental stigma attached to these unresolved conflicts than in the adult. This aspect of normalcy is a great boon to the attitude of the therapist and can help set the tone of the therapeutic atmosphere. It can be of great value in the therapist's acceptance of the adolescent and his needs. Furthermore, it often is an aid in offsetting unconscious countertransference problems and resistances in the therapist. We say comfortingly to ourselves, "The adolescent is going through a difficult phase." Thus, in dealing with this age group, one cannot overstress certain requirements for the therapist. In addition to dynamic understanding, flexibility and ingenuity as well as consistency and enduring patience and genuine interest are essential for success.

The preceding chapters have all emphasized the importance of the therapist's allying himself with the adolescent's needs; therefore it may be well to put in a few words stressing the value of offering a healthy resistance to the adolescent against which he may fight, and in the exercise of struggle, gain strength which can be obtained only through such actual struggle. I was much interested in an example of this in a panel discussion devoted to the problems of adolescence. A boy of seventeen, who was a member of the panel, engaged in a debate with his own father, who was a member of the audience. Both held stoutly to their own points of view and argued enthusiastically. But although there was good humor, there also was serious struggle in their argument. The boy's strength and adequacy were apparent, but it was obvious that he had had much practice in serious, though amicable struggle with a father who obviously respected his son's right to a point of view of his own and encouraged the son to stand up for it.

This principle of the "good fight," while a readily acceptable concept, is difficult to achieve either in living or in therapy, inasmuch as it presupposes optimum or near optimum management of the hostile impulses by a strong and constructively disposed ego and superego. When guilt and punishment motives dominate, or the ego strength is insufficient for constructive control, the impulses are often employed toward destructive ends and the "good fight" becomes a "bad fight" which to some degree may leave temporary or permanent marks. Such detrimental effects are particularly evident in various degrees and types of negative countertransference where the therapist either consciously or unconsciously gets involved in any of a number of struggles with an adolescent, which may well repeat the blunders that the parents have made. On the other hand, in the milieu of a positive relationship, constructive "battles" can be extremely valuable therapeutically and, in the hands of a skillful therapist, are invaluable ego-building aids especially in this adolescent period.

In summary, I would like to say that these interesting chapters amply verify the fact that adolescents' needs differ widely. In addition, they all elaborate on the following themes which I have chosen to emphasize: (1) the importance for successful therapy of a dynamic understanding of the specific conflicts and needs of the adolescent; (2) willingness on the part of the therapist to ally himself with these needs as the adolescent presents them to us; and (3) help for the adolescent which enables him to correct the blunders of the past through a consistent and patient cooperation.

Thus, through our understanding, skillfully applied in an alliance with the young person's constructive potential, we may help him to attain mastery of his impulses and to find realistic ways of fulfilling them.

8

A PSYCHOTHERAPEUTIC INTERVIEW WITH AN ADOLESCENT

A Recording with Dynamic Comments

RUBEN R. POTTASH, M.D.

INTRODUCTION

The following is a verbatim typescript of a tape-recorded twenty-minute interview. The analytical commentary is set in italics and inserted in brackets to distinguish it from the actual responses in the interview.

The patient is an eighteen-year-old boy, first seen by the author (then his family physician) about six years before this session. At that time, when he was twelve, he was complaining of "stomach trouble," compulsive eating and obesity. He was referred then to a psychiatric clinic in Philadelphia.

In the interim, his family also became the writer's patients. It became apparent that there was constant and pointless arguing between father and son. About a week before this interview, the father was sent to a hospital with a tumor which was at first feared to be malignant but later proven benign.

The patient is tall and heavy, rather immature in manner, and speaks with a boyish voice.

D. Tell me how you are feeling and when it started, can you?

P. I think so. I feel, I don't know, I feel at ease with certain people and with others I don't feel at ease. Like I'd say

it started when my father got sick. I . . . I sort of took
it on myself. I thought maybe it was my fault when my
father got sick. I know that things have not been too
smoothly at home. I was out of work all summer and
there were many arguments, so when my father got
sick I thought maybe it was my fault but that feeling
went away, of course. But my nerves haven't been the
same since that.

[*The first statement that the patient makes contains the
nuclear problem as well as the indicated approach. In
saying, "I feel at ease with certain people," he is telling
the therapist that he may view him differently from the
way he does his father, i.e., that he wants to visualize him
as a good father surrogate, who does not retaliate or
provoke guilt, and not as an object of hostility or envy.
He then goes on to say that the feeling started when his
father got sick and that, in some way, it may have been
his fault. If this is so (i.e., to be confirmed by later material), then the problem is guilt based on envy. For
maximum effectiveness and conciseness, the therapist
should direct the interview toward evaluating, elucidat-
ing and clarifying this almost conscious hostility and
envy, while capitalizing on and maintaining the benign
role that the patient has putatively assigned him.*]

D. Since he got sick?

[*The therapist points up the temporal relationship and
infers the causative relationship.*]

P. That's right—I just seem to be ill at ease—now I mean I
am talking to you—I feel natural now. With certain
people I do, but at home I don't. I don't understand it.

[*The patient reaffirms his readiness to relate positively to
the therapist.*]

D. You spoke before about feeling disappointed.

[*In the short period before the tape recording began, the*

patient spoke about a vague feeling of disappointment. It
was appropriate therefore at this point to bring the feel-
ing of disappointment into the constellation of envy, hos-
tility, guilt and consequent depression. (Disappointment
could only be based on the fact that some expected thing
had failed to happen as he hoped it would, i.e., that his
father would die and that he would be the mother's only
object.)]

P. I have a depressed feeling, I,—it's so hard to explain—I
    feel like I am waiting for something to happen and it's
    never going to happen—and I feel like I gotta run
    away and I go out of the house and—well I want to go
    right back home again. I know there's nothing out of
    the house. I don't have too many friends. I was going
    with a buddy but he is down South now and I have a
    feeling—and I have a lonesome feeling to tell you the
    truth. (Sighs) I don't know—I don't know what I'm
    looking for—forward to something that's not going to
    happen.

[The patient restates the problem and then expresses his
feeling of hopeless loneliness (a motivation for his hostile
wishes).]

D. Is it dreadful, do you think, what might happen or it is
    pleasant?

[The therapist at this point has a feeling for the dynamics
and is structuring the interview so that it will result in a
specific statement that the death of the father and the
exclusive possession of the mother is the expected event
that has not and cannot happen. This is all really cen-
tered on the therapist's re-use of the word "happen,"
which commits the interview to an ultimately deep in-
terpretation of the patient's unconscious fantasies.]

P. Well, that's just it, I don't know. (Pause) I've been going
    out very seldom now. I stay around the house all the

time—I'm working in the store all the time, and well I go to the movies, that's all. We close now Thursday night and Sunday night, but I go to the movies or I go to a friend's house or relatives. But Saturday night was the first time I went out for a long time since my father's been sick. That happened so suddenly. On a couple minutes' notice I went out. But when I got up Sunday morning I felt alright until I started to get a depressed feeling. I couldn't understand what it was and I thought maybe I was sick or something—because I have had pains in my stomach all the time and my mother kept saying, "Why don't you go to the doctor," and I thought maybe I'll put it off until tomorrow and it will go away.

[*The patient answers in terms of loneliness again. He then describes his various primitive modes of dealing with the conflict, i.e., withdrawal and somatization. He is making an unconscious attempt to withdraw from further exploration of the problem as well as to identify with the father.*]

D. Do you have any idea what you might be depressed about?
   (Pause)

[*This is a reflective and unstructured question encouraging the patient to go further into the unconscious.*]

P. I dunno. I thought it might be that I'm lonesome. You know, I feel like I'm alone. Even when I'm with a lot of people I feel like I'm alone.

[*Again the feeling of loneliness. His inability to find relatedness is partly the original motive of his unconscious "crime" of hostility against his rival father and partly an appropriate punishment for himself, the "criminal." He implies his assent to go further into the unconscious in order to be related to the therapist.*]

D. Hasn't it always been that way?

[*The therapist makes a bid for further material, particularly infantile memories or habitual reaction patterns. He invokes the patient's consideration of self, by being accepting of that self.*]

P. Not as much as it is lately. Now when I was working it was alright, but when I am not working it isn't like that. I can't get a job. I mean everybody I've tried—so many places, and they all tell you when you're going in the service—now my father tells me to join the service—not to enlist, to register for the draft. I mean to go up like that (ill at ease) but I don't want to. I don't know why. I just don't want to.

[*The patient brings the problem into present reality. He feels displaced. He accuses his father, in effect, of inviting him to leave home; he does not want to surrender to his rival.*]

D. Do you look forward to being in the service with some dread too?

[*Uses word "dread" to establish a link with the primitive drama of the unconscious. The patient denies this on reality grounds.*]

P. No, not any particular dread—I feel like if I have to go I have to go. Everybody's going but, I mean, there's no use running into it. If it's going to come, it's going to come.

[*He has no dread of realistic and impersonal danger. (He dreads and resists, however, what he unconsciously believes to be his father's retaliatory murderous wishes.)*]

D. Have you been arguing with your father a lot?

[*This is a response to the patient's implication that his "dread" problem is with his father.*]

P. I used to, but I haven't argued with him since he was sick.
  [*The patient defensively claims to have reformed.*]

D. Before?
  [*The therapist does not allow the patient to mask the repressed hostility from himself.*]

P. Yes.
  [*The patient shows reluctance to speak about the previous period and thus to weaken his present repression.*]

D. What about mostly?
  [*Another push toward further exploration and acceptance of hostile attitudes.*]

P. Well, I don't know. (Pause) It's just things in general. I mean he used to—if I would say something, if I would be talking to my mother, he would interfere and I would tell him that I didn't want him to interfere when I was talking to my mother. I've never been close to my father really, really close, cause I don't know, I was always next to my mother in everything. My father, I always looked upon my father as an outsider—as someone who was interfering, in the way—and so we used to argue over absolutely nothing.

  [*This is the conscious and explicit statement of the pre-previously unconscious infantile fantasy that he was exclusively with mother and that father was an outsider. The patient cannot face his unconscious wishes that his father would die and make the fantasy real, since these wishes give rise to guilt. But neither can he handle the disappointment that his father is still alive because of the intensity of his need for mother's exclusive love. (Nonetheless the boy's attitude toward the therapist clearly indicates his deeply unconscious desire for a live father who could accept these envious feelings and not reciprocate with hate. Only in the presence of such acceptance will*] *the patient be able, in turn, first to accept and then re-linquish his negative wishes and thus achieve a positive identification with the father figure.)]*

D. When did you realize that you looked on your father as an outsider? Was it always like that?

[*The therapist attempts to clarify in the patient's mind the fact that this conflict goes back to childhood aspirations.*]

P. As long as I can remember it's always been like that, but I realized it when he got sick.

[*The patient agrees and now begins to understand why the present-day situation has been traumatic.*]

D. How did you realize it more then?

[*The therapist attempts to integrate past and present, i.e., the patient's childhood envy with his current anxiety over father's potentially serious illness. Once this new insight is established, the aim of the interview will very likely be realized.*]

P. Cause I saw how hard it was on my mother—you see I thought—I always had the feeling that if my father wasn't there it wouldn't make any difference. But when I saw how it affected my mother when he was sick I realized then—I realized right then—that it certainly would be a difference if I was with my mother alone—rather than my father was with her cause I realized it wouldn't make that much difference if I wasn't there. That's the way I figured it.

[*The patient says, in effect, "I am disappointed, lonely and depressed, because I see that father is chosen by mother rather than me. My hostile wishes toward him are of no use, even if they were to come true."*]

D. Uh—huh. Well what did you think about it from there?

[*The therapist merely expresses attention in order to give the patient a little push to continue in the same line.*]

P. I still feel the same way. We haven't been arguing now—
we're getting along very well and I (Pause) well, once
in a while I used to argue with my mother too, but like
I say, since my father has been sick we haven't been
arguing at all. (Pause)

[*The patient has been frightened and is succeeding in
suppressing overt expression of the old hostility. He has
turned it inward. His depression is the result of his in-
hibition.*]

D. What are you thinking right now?

[*This is a nondirective question that again gives the patient a chance to go on or to retreat if the material is too
overwhelming.*]

P. (Loud) I'm thinking of how to tell you how it feels the
way I was depressed yesterday. I went around moping
yesterday. I didn't know what to do—what to look for.
I wanted to amuse myself just to entertain myself—I
put a radio on—I turned it off—I put TV on—I
played records—and I couldn't find what I was looking
for.

[*As the patient goes on with the description of his affects,
he unconsciously appeals for the therapist's sympathy and
approval on the grounds that he has repressed his hostility.*]

D. Did you feed yourself?

[*The therapist gives recognition to the extent of the patient's conflict and regression by making explicit this
boy's well-known mode of defense.*]

P. That's my weakest thing. I'm on one of my own diets
right now. So that's another thing—whenever I used
to become upset I used to eat and eat and eat and I'd
forget about it, but I can't do that now, I'm trying not
to anyway.

[*The patient understands that oral satisfaction is no solution to the present problem.*]

D. How did you make out yesterday?

[*The therapist attempts to give this feeling a chance for more verbalization. He offers the patient support by stressing his role of a benign parent.*]

P. Oh, pretty good. In fact I think I ate less yesterday but now, last night, I happened to run into my next-door neighbor and her husband was out, so she asked me if I'd walk with her—she has a dog—that was the first time I'd felt better all day long. I went out around 8:30 and we were walking around and I went in and had coffee with her—came home about 11 o'clock and that's the only time the tension seemed to go—when I was with somebody I could talk to. But it's not the same when I talk to my parents.

[*The patient describes a mild instance of acting out the oedipal drama with his neighbor's wife, and the relief it brought him. This shows further insight, at least by implication, that his problem is not to be solved by oral satisfaction but by some more mature form of libidinal gratification.*]

D. What would you have done—your father had a pretty serious operation—what would you have done if he had died? Did you think about it?

[*The therapist presents the problem of hostility directly. He softens the impact by reminding the patient at the same time of present reality factors. The patient's good reality testing (evidenced by the patient's response above) has convinced him that the boy's ego is strong enough to assimilate this unconscious material in the presence of a supporting and accepting father in the person of a therapist.*]

P. I thought about it a lot—we thought he was going to die (very softly) and, I don't know, I guess—we would have just stayed on until we could—I would help my mother as much as I could.

[*The patient begins to admit that he has thought of what might happen if his infantile wishes were gratified (i.e., by his father's death). He then hesitates and withdraws from accepting further insight by taking the position of a dutiful son habitually concerned for his mother.*]

D. Did you picture how it might be at home if he *were* dead?

[*The therapist feels that the patient is on the edge of accepting this crucial piece of insight. He therefore gives a further push in the same direction, by means of virtually repeating the same question.*]

P. It would be very lonesome at home, would have been terrible for my mother and then my mother would not have been able to stand it, cause, you see whenever he went away or something—it wasn't like him getting sick—I thought good riddance and I could always get around my mother much easier than my father. Although if I asked my father for something he would give it to me, but it wouldn't be like asking my mother for it. She would give it to me and say something, some little thing. I can't recall right away, but my father would just give it to me "here" and good-by. It got to a very serious point. We would just say "hello" and "good-by" to each other, and wouldn't talk to each other at all after that.

[*The patient takes the plunge into verbalizing his readily accessible hostility toward his father.*]

D. You were sort of mad at each other?

[*The therapist summarizes what the patient is saying and puts into words the strength of the id drive.*]

P. Well, he was indifferent in a general way. He sort of took the same viewpoint I took. If I was friendly, he was friendly. If I wasn't, he wouldn't. I suppose that's the way he looked at it.

[The patient acknowledges that the drive is his own without the need to project it onto father.]

D. But you said you had thought a lot about what would happen if your father died. How would you have taken it?

[The therapist invites the patient to verbalize his feelings but holds him to the main theme.]

P. (Pause) I don't know, I know the day that he was operated on my mother was gone and I was by myself—she was down at the hospital and I was near out of my mind. I was just very upset. I was actually crying and I don't remember when I cried before that—all day long I was carrying on until she called me. I told her to call me right away and when she called me I remember I—I felt like—I had a funny feeling when she told me that it was alright. I felt like some—I don't know whether I felt disappointed—it's terrible to say I don't know whether I felt disappointed or what. You know you look forward to something and then you don't know if it's going to happen. I think if he had died, I would have felt the same way. You are waiting for an answer—no matter what it is you want to hear that answer—yes or no—if he is better or if he is worse—like a weight being lifted off of you.

[The patient experiences the release of affective response. This is the first time, although indirectly, that his ego has accepted his formerly unconscious wish for his father's death.]

D. Well, as you said when you came in, you've been going around lately feeling disappointed.

[*The therapist is helping to relate ego and id (affect and cause).*]

P. (Long pause) Well, you don't think it's *that,* do you?

[*In a tentative way, the patient's ego achieves direct acceptance of his id wishes.*]

D. I don't think it's what?

[*This is a pretense of naiveté so that the patient is pushed to further expression of these wishes.*]

P. My father is still—that he got better?

[*Guilt causes the patient to interrupt and deny his full thought, i.e., "Am I disappointed that my father did not die?"*]

D. Well, I don't know, *you* just said it.

[*The therapist says in effect, "These are your wishes, as you now understand them, not a piece of imagination or theoretical construction."*]

P. I don't think it's that. (Pause) Cause right now, I mean, if it wasn't my father and mother, I wouldn't know what to do because I can't get a job now. I *am* dependent on them. My buddy went to Norfolk, Va. last year and he said several times, "Come on down," he has a job for me and everything. My mother said if I want to go, I can go but I don't want to. I want to stay home with them.

[*The patient rejects responsibility for any hostile feelings. He says further, "I'm just a little boy and I really need their love and care."*]

D. You mean with *her?*

[*The therapist says, "You pretend to be little and helpless, but you have not completely given up the hope of having your mother for yourself."*]

P. Well, with both of them now.

[*This is a partial denial of the therapist's interpretation, but has also an undertone of a revised, perhaps more mature feeling about his father.*]

D. Now?

[*This is said in order to bring out the undertone of a changed feeling to father. With the main theme now conscious, the interview goes into a phase of working through, i.e., recapitulation and solidification of new insight, so that the patient may have a base from which to solve the problem.*]

P. Yes.

D. Since when?

P. Well, since my father got better.

[*"The illness made a change in my emotional relation to my father."*]

D. What are you smiling about? (In a light tone)

[*The therapist notes the change of affect.*]

P. (Laughs) I don't know.

D. Something struck you a little bit funny.

P. Well, when you said "since when"—that's, I mean that did strike me funny the way you said that—you seem to think that I am saying I am sorry he got better, and I'm not.

D. You're not sorry that he got better?

P. No, I'm not sorry—I'm glad that he got better.

D. Well, alright.

P. (Laughs)

[*A curious interchange takes place here. The patient is smiling at the release of guilt and the acceptance of an insight and then goes on to say something which is grammatically correct, but the affect strikes the therapist as the opposite of what the patient really says. The slip may be thought of as implicit rather than explicit. He attempts to analyze it, but realizes that this will be uneco-*

*nomical of time and effort and perhaps not worth while
enough in terms of insight. Therefore he drops it without
further explanation. By this time, the statement: "I'm
glad he got better" begins to be true because the patient
is glad to be released from an unresolved oedipal situation.*]

D. For a guy who is depressed you're doing an awful lot of
  laughing right now.

  [*The therapist accepts the patient's pleasure in his release.*]

P. This is the first time I have laughed all day.

  [*The patient confirms it.*]

D. Maybe there is something in this "joke" about your wish-
  ing he would get better or not get better?

  [*The therapist says, "The change in feeling is due to
  something you have learned here."*]

P. No, I don't know anything about that. (Softly)

  [*The patient denies, almost as a formality, the insight.*]

D. Well, let's see, does that fit in with what you were telling
  me before about the fact that you picture how you
  were closer to your mother than he was, or staying
  with her?

  [*The therapist goes on, seeming to ignore the denial.*]

P. I thought that (note of protest in voice) he was interfering. If I would say something to my mother, he would
  say, "What did he say?" And I would say, I would tell
  him I was talking to my mother, wasn't talking to him.
  I don't know why I was like that—I thought of it so
  many times to figure it out why it was like that.
  Couldn't do it.

  [*The therapist's conviction and the patient's halfhearted
  denial result in an affective response that seeks to justify
  the pure childish hostility to father.*]

D. Well, at the same time you were talking to "my mother" you were talking to *his* "wife."

[*"Your ego should be handling this."* At this point the therapist is helping the patient set up an ideal than can strengthen his ego and thus free him both from punitive conscience and overwhelming impulse.]

P. That's right—but I didn't realize that, I mean, of course I knew it but I never looked at it in that way (pause) and (reflectively) and all the time I was wrong.

[*"I believe I can face this problem and handle it"* (ego-syntonically).]

D. How do you mean wrong?

[*"Are you sure you are handling it with ego, not super-ego?"*]

P. (Laughs) Cause now, I look at it in a different light.

[*"Ego."*]

D. Since when?

[*This is a bid for restatement and consolidation of the problem by the patient so that the therapist may check that some actual emotional acceptance and working through have taken place and that there has been a resultant gain in ego strength. The patient gives an adequate answer to the bid.*]

P. (Laughs again) Since he got better. You understand it's a big thing to—to realize in such a short time.

[*The therapist agrees, with warmth, that patient has done a good piece of work.*]

P. It is—such a short time to realize that—because for nineteen years I mean, I looked at it the other way. Now, I'm not bothering about actually going out of my way to please him. If he wants something, I'd do it for him. If he wants me to go some place for him, I go some place for him.

[*The superego comes up here in terms of, "I am a good little boy."*]

D. Well, maybe this is *another* piece of the disappointment.

[*The therapist alludes to the repressed affect implied in the humility.*]

P. How do you mean?

D. Well, suppose for nineteen years you had hopes of being with your mother exclusively. What did you suddenly realize?

[*The therapist makes a bald statement of the oedipal situation so that the ego will be forced to give up the restrictive (though protective) humility.*]

P. (Pause) I suddenly realized that being with my mother— that my mother wouldn't be happy with me alone.

[*This is a new view of a very old problem; "Not only father, but mother, and perhaps even myself would suffer if I got my wish."*]

D. Well, that would be pretty damn disappointing, wouldn't it?

[*The therapist appeals to the reality principle, i.e., "You can't win, so why not quit?"*]

P. Well, sure.

D. So you come in to tell me you have this vague feeling of being disappointed. Maybe the feeling of disappointment that you are talking about is made up of a couple of feelings.

[*The therapist invites further exploration because both the patient and he are now agreed on the necessity for a new solution.*]

P. (Complaining) I have the feeling of being depressed, of being left out of something.

[*The patient expresses his feeling of loneliness. This problem has yet to be solved.*]

D. Left out of what? You just said it.

[*The therapist is reassuring and tries to help the patient further so that he can see what is making him lonely and thereby ultimately arrive at a more satisfactory solution.*]

P. All right, (belligerently) I, I see people having a good time, I feel like I'm being left out of that. It's very hard for me to laugh lately. I can't laugh—I look at TV and I don't enjoy it. I went to the movies Sunday night—I always enjoy going to the movies—I know the time when I went to the movies seven times a week, too. I walked out of the movie, I couldn't stand it in there.

D. What about this feeling of being left out?

P. (Pause) Well, when I went out Saturday night, we all had a good time, but Sunday, I don't know, I felt like I wasn't having a good time any more. You can't always have a good time and yet when I go out to work, I feel like I'm a part of it.

[*After the preceding catharsis, the patient begins to perceive that there are other worlds besides the family constellation.*]

D. If your mother is going to do better with your father than with you—don't you think you're going to be left out?

[*The therapist clearly encourages this perception of the futility of being a "hanger on."*]

P. No, because I think my mother has room for two—she can side with both of us.

[*Rather suddenly the patient begins to feel that the complaint of being left out is not so justified now. What is surprising is the jump in the logical development that the therapist had expected. The patient here seems both to give up his complaint and emerge with his new insight all in one sentence.*]

D. If you're two different people?

[*The therapist jumps with him and accepts the more rapid advance. He attempts to get the patient to realize more clearly his new feeling about the family relationship, especially as it regards his father.*]

P. That's right.

[*The patient understands himself and feels understood.*]

D. If you don't compete?

[*An additional step in clarifying the patient's basic feelings to his father.*]

P. That's right, we're just united together.

D. And so you are now—I don't think that was your picture before for nineteen years?

[*The therapist encourages more realistic and contemporary appraisal of the former distortions.*]

P. No, it was a competition—it was a struggle—who was going to survive, my father or myself.

[*This sentence can hardly be more true or more primitive. The ego must feel full control at this point in order to allow the patient the freedom to say this.*]

D. So, what is the outcome?

[*The therapist gives recognition of this new ego control by handing the problem back to the patient to solve.*]

P. So, when my father was getting sick, I saw that he was not surviving, I saw also that I wasn't going to either. Either both of us or none of us. (Softly) So now it seems that we're united a little. But I still have this feeling. If that feeling was gone, it would be different.

[*The patient gets ready to take responsibility by a clear and dramatic recapitulation. However, he knows that the vestiges of the infantile struggle must still be dealt with.*]

D. I think the feeling that you have actually of being left out is of being left out of this dream of being the only

one with her. Like everybody is having a good time—
that is, they have somebody. Everybody has somebody
except you. Your mother has your father, your father
has your mother, you have nothing. When did you
break up with your girl friend?

[*The therapist refers to the patient's previous ideas as a*
"dream." By dramatizing the feelings in that dream he
helps the boy externalize them. However, the therapist
accepts the instinctual demand incorporated in the dream
and obliquely, but clearly, invites the patient to the
libidinal gratification appropriate to his age. This is an
extension of the benign father role.]

P. Pardon, when did I break up with her?

[*It is hard to come back to reality.*]

D. Yes.

P. About a year ago. Her mother thought that she was too
young and since then I haven't gone out with a girl.
No, I've gone out with a girl a couple of times, but
nothing to speak about. But that was an awful disappointment too, because when I was going out with my
girl, I wasn't so, I didn't feel so bad against my father.
I even brought the girl over to the house a couple of
times and my mother and father both liked her a lot.
But we seemed to have gotten along better at that time
too.

[*With current and realistic interest, the patient notes that*
"when I was going out with my girl, I didn't feel so bad
against my father"; i.e., he has heard the suggestion and
agrees with it on the basis of his past and actual experi-
ence.]

D. So when you had your own, you didn't want his?

[*The therapist shows his acceptance and respect by a kind*
of man-to-man talk.]

P. I guess you're right.

[*The patient accepts the insight.*]

D. Now, you're *way* left out. Like left field?

P. Even further back. (Laughs) My father was disappointed when I did not graduate at high school. He was disappointed when I quit my first job. He was disappointed about that too, because I could not find a job afterward. My mother went down to the shore last summer, I was with my father alone, for a week—I only stayed three days and I went down to the shore. So I see what you mean now. I never realized it. I was never with them anyway. I went out from dawn until I had to go to bed.

[*The patient is able to realize that his previous behavior has not been mature and cites chapter and verse.*]

D. Makes a little more sense now?

[*The therapist continues to give something worth while and constructive to identify with.*]

P. That's right. (Softly)

D. You shaking your head yes?

[*The observation is technically necessary because this interview is recorded on tape and a listener would have to know what the boy was doing.*]

P. Yes, I am shaking my head. Yes, I'm shaking my head because I'm starting to realize it now.

[*"I'm working on this thing."*]

D. You know that's almost as big a thing to realize as the "nineteen-year" thing.

[*The "nineteen-year-thing" refers to the patient's competitive struggle with father. The patient had previously used "nineteen years" as a measure of the extent of his problem. This piece of realization has further to do with*] *his "abandoning" mother as someone who really belongs to father anyway.*]

P. (Pause) Can a person change so suddenly?

["*Do you think I can do it?*"]

D. Sometimes. When you are young and elastic. Like you are. You have a lot of bend to you—you have a lot of "give." You have the room to change—they haven't. They're pretty old and stodgy and stuck. You have room enough to get over this, which is really a sort of a little boy's heartbreak. Most kids get over this by the time they are six.

[*The therapist, in effect, philosophizes so that the patient can get some perspective. This will allow him to look back on the trauma in a way that is benign rather than self-destructive. Perspective is accomplished through the strength of the mutual identification.*]

P. Uh, huh.

[*The patient is musing and assimilating.*]

D. You're a great big boy—but inside I think you're a little one. Maybe you can start to grow up a little more now. Maybe get a girl of your own—instead of the one "just like the one that married dear old dad."

[*The therapist points out that the reward for giving up the infantile position is really an equivalent to the satisfaction for which the patient originally strove. He also recognizes, however, that the new-found insight is not yet stable and that regressions are bound to occur in the future.*]

P. I see what you mean. (Pause) That's what I'll have to do I guess.

[*The patient understands and agrees in effect to try to go forward in a way more appropriate to his age.*]

D. Well, I'll tell you what you do—you think about it for a
   while and then I'd like to see you or hear from you
   and talk to you about this a little further. We'll give it
   another crack a little later on. Why don't you give me
   a call here Friday? We'll give you a little time to chew
   this over and digest it. We'll go from there and see
   what has to be done.

   [*This is a good place to terminate the interview. The
   problem has been fairly well stated, explored, and con-
   solidated. A satisfactory solution has been suggested and
   tentatively accepted. It is interesting that the therapist
   uses the terminology of orality (i.e., "chew this over and
   digest it"), thus intuitively acknowledging that in spite of
   the main theme much of the problem is preoedipal.*]

P. All right.

9

THE PSYCHOTHERAPY OF THE ADOLESCENT FROM A SCHOOLMASTER'S POINT OF VIEW

C. THURSTON CHASE

THE SETTING

This chapter is based upon a schoolmaster's rather close observation of more than 1,250 adolescents and preadolescents over a thirty-year period. Twenty-seven years of this time the writer has spent in the capacity of headmaster of a relatively small (100-150 students) boarding school for boys from the third through the tenth grade. The great bulk of the experience has been with the years commonly known as those of "Junior High School."

At one time or another the population of the school has been drawn from practically every State in the Union and from some twenty-five or more foreign countries. My remarks will deal almost entirely with American students whose home backgrounds are relatively homogeneous, and which represent a definitely recognizable segment of this country's population.

The reader will recall that the population of the independent schools in this country, excluding those which are essentially religious in nature, is only about 2 per cent of the total school population. These students come chiefly from homes that are in an economically and culturally favored position. A large proportion of the parents have had college or other higher educational experience. We, like most independent schools, make a practice of seeking out the promising student, whose family income cannot provide independent education, to receive financial help through scholarship grants. Such boys are not identified within the school and are on a footing of complete equality with their classmates. Selection of students is exercised for intellectual and leadership potential, rather than based on economic or social position. Thus our school population is reasonably varied and representative in home background.

We strive to provide a homelike atmosphere. Contacts between parents and teachers are, for the most part, so frank, real and personal that it can be said that the School's knowledge of their families is usually as great as, and often greater than, that which might be obtained by the average day school. Social contacts with girls, through games and parties, are sufficiently frequent and natural to provide some knowledge of the part that boy-girl relationships may play in the life of the students.

Although my remarks are based chiefly upon our own experience, they are also influenced by the experience of other schoolmasters in both boys' and girls' boarding and day schools. Some of these groups are much less selected than our own. Thus I hope this chapter will have some general applicability.

TRUSTING PARTNERSHIP

Many schoolmasters strongly agree with the plea made earlier in this book for more and better professional care and guidance by psychological experts specifically trained to help youth. Only very recently have specialized adolescent services, such as the Adolescent Unit of the Children's Medical Center in Boston, begun to make their greatly needed contribution, which school teachers hope may be vastly multiplied and extended throughout the country.

Few topics have had more attention in current popular literature than child psychology and guidance, yet in our culture adolescence has long lacked appeal, interest and attention. I suspect that many adults—professionals as well as parents—would find difficulty or feel shame in vividly re-creating many aspects of their own youth. The foibles or strains of earlier childhood have seemed more attractive and forgivable. How else could so many jibes have gained and maintained popularity? "Adolescence is like the winter snow and ice—if you survive, it will melt away"; "Adolescence is not a period—it's a comma"—are typical. Have we not joined in these, too? Must not many of us who deal professionally with adolescents admit that we have unconsciously tended to push our own youthful struggles back in our memory, thereby handicapping our full identification with the young people whom we want to help? High in importance among the challenges to both psychiatrists and teachers is the absolute necessity of giving to the popular conception of adolescence a wholesome "normalcy," respectability, and yes—the glory that the era deserves.

Our most thoughtful citizens today feel deep concern for the adolescent. A prominent physician, the able and understanding father of a large family, wrote me recently: "I cannot help but feel that there is a restlessness among our youth of today that defies all reason and understanding. They are challenging us as to whether we are using good judgment or not. They seem to want to feel that they are adults long before they are ready and, if they are to be reprimanded, they take it as a personal affront and immediately wish to seek vengeance." Surely, cooperation between psychiatrist and teacher can do much to heal the growing "split between the generations" (45, p. 680) that threatens to become a characteristic of our contemporary culture.

Obvious public alarm over juvenile delinquency further dramatizes the urgency of the plea for more trained personnel and psychotherapeutic facilities. I believe that our failure to understand the adolescent, to give him status, and adequate professional help when needed, is responsible not only for a substantial share of the ever-increasing rate of mental illness, but for the more frightening fact that a growing number of our population appear to be failing to reach full emotional maturity in their so-called adulthood.

The concern of nearly all good schools and good teachers with their students' emotional needs is very great—far greater than is generally realized. Some study in psychology is an almost universal requirement for the teaching profession. Despite the barrenness of many of the formal teacher-training courses, psychological understanding is far and away the greatest topic of leisure-time reading and discussion throughout the profession. All the professional publications, educational conferences and faculty gatherings substantiate this. Yet sometimes we in the school world feel that we have been considered by psychiatrists as relatively uninformed and untrained. At times this has created resentment and division between those who specialize and those who apply the same underlying principles in every phase of their daily work. A more trusting partnership is needed.

Recently a psychiatrist friend asked me, "When will you learn that the adolescent is the normal schizophrenic?" I had always been content with the German characterization of the period as *"Sturm und Drang!"* or that of William Sturm, *"Ich Findung."* Yet if one accepts, even to a moderate degree, my friend's premise that adolescence can be considered as a developmental "illness," unavoidable and necessary for the growth of the mature self, and of those characteristics of realistic acceptance and personality development which we term adulthood, then the urgency of further knowledge about this illness, or "phase," if we prefer the term, is exceedingly vital for all who deal with it.

We teachers have come to understand that instability is

normal and that very simple and necessary inner conflicts can produce diverse and socially alarming manifestations! We know that deviation and excess are generally inherent in this period. The person professionally engaged with youth must and usually does expect the dramatic and the tumultuous, and accepts these extremes as normal at a time when life forces, environment and interpersonal relations are more vivid and vital than at any other.

The adolescent is *ipso facto* a somewhat disturbed person who, however "normal" he may be, requires at least a mild and continuous therapy from parents and teacher. Conversely, the good teacher of youth is, *ipso facto,* a lay therapist. If a youth's parents and home are falling short of meeting his needs, as seems to be increasingly true in today's American culture, the teacher must be ever more knowledgeable and skillful in emotional guidance—even if enough psychiatrists do become available for the really ill young people.

There is urgent need for more and better psychological training of junior and senior high school teachers, as well as for a marked increase in confidence and cooperation between psychiatrist and teacher. Those schools which have a staff psychiatrist, or a regular consultant, are fortunate, for the trained expert can become the teacher of the teacher, and simultaneously learn much about the environment and guidance of his charges. Often the school physician, although not a psychiatrist, will have background and training to help.

An invaluable social service would be performed if the psychological profession, facing its own inadequacy in numbers and in facilities for the adolescent, sought to bridge the gap by taking the initiative in setting up far better training and advisory facilities for teachers. They in turn would, I am convinced, respond to the opportunity in such numbers, and with such warmth, as to surprise the professional.

"Never-never Land"

Probably no other culture has existed which holds the adolescent in so unfavorable a light as our own. Primitive cultures lay great stress upon the preparation of the child for adulthood, provide painstaking guidance and preparation for it, and attribute far more significance to the attainment of its status. The reaching of puberty is generally looked forward to and celebrated by rites which give it dignity and acceptance. Very careful tutoring and guided experience is also given to the youth, whether male or female, who is beginning to assume both the biological and social responsibilities of the adult. In primitive civilizations, the adolescent is provided a highly structured era of development. In feudal civilizations, he was granted much useful responsibility and apprenticeship. In pioneer civilizations he was needed as the companion and helper of the adult of his own sex, with whom identification and sharing were immediately possible, and, in fact, necessary.

We today make the era a "never-never land." In an unstructured vacuum, we treat our adolescents as a lost group—clumsy, unattractive, troubled—as in a world apart from either the children they no longer are, or the adults whom they have not yet become. It might well be reflected that these social attitudes toward youth are a thorough abnegation of the responsibilities of a democracy *which calls for competent individuals as citizens.* Could this denial come from our own subconscious rejections of the memories of youth when our feelings were in such conflict with the dogmatic Victorian or Puritan mores of our parents' world?

We have accepted the necessity of what we call "sex education for children," the teaching of simple fundamentals of reproduction and growth.[1] Yet who of us can say that the

---

[1] In addition to the many increasingly excellent books in this field, we recommend for older children and preadolescents the Oregon Film, "Human Growth."

average adolescent is given much help along the line of his first psychological need, the acceptance of his or her own body, in the period when this is of the utmost importance to him? The best we now provide are books or classes on social behavior with the opposite sex! As yet, no open or prideful guidance dealing with the "self-power" of the life force is offered our young man or woman until the late teen-agers are given "premarital homemaking" instruction. We all know the extent to which early sexual guilt, fears and conflicts cause adolescent maladjustment, and how they may produce later mental illness. Yet here there is a glaring area of neglect which no other civilization would tolerate. Of course, the job should be the parents'—but what they so often shirk or fumble, the psychiatrist and the teachers *must* fill in.

Since "adolescence" has been so generally assumed to be specifically the years between puberty and full manhood or womanhood (whatever that may be!) it seems well to say a few words about its onset and conclusion. We must not forget that, in all growth, nature's changes are gradual. The obvious is preceded, and prepared for, by less noticeable but powerfully important forces. Dr. William Greulich, in his studies and indices of sexual maturity, gives clear evidence of the gradualness of preadolescent influence of the hormones. We know that X-rays of the epiphyses will give evidence of oncoming change, and remarkably accurate prediction of the clear-cut onset of puberty. Since the physical forces are demonstrably at work between the ages of ten and thirteen (some researchers say even as early as eight), should we not assume that "preadolescence" will be influenced to foreshadow also the psychological characteristics of adolescence itself? Surely the social influence of the thirteenth, fourteenth and fifteenth years is powerful upon the three that precede. Gesell, Ilg, and Ames (21) choose the years "from ten to sixteen" as a unit. It opens and closes with a "nodal" year. Throughout the intervening period they have identified a homogeneity of symptom and behavior which is consistent in its conflicts, its swings, and its variations—a unit of transitional growth which, in this schoolmaster's observation, seems sound and well chosen as a developmental era to replace the former concept of thirteen to twenty.

A few youths may carry unresolved early adolescent conflicts and confusions beyond the normal era. Yet, after sixteen, most of the still "teen-age" youngsters will have, we hope, developed sufficient ego, confidence and personality to depend upon themselves. Then they will be more ready to seek and receive adult guidance with some degree of equanimity and with acceptance on both sides. This writer feels that the real crisis and its resolution are nearly always reached by sixteen, and that it is those years immediately preceding which call for the ultimate of adult understanding, tolerance and friendship.

The School's Responsibility for Mental Health

General

Most schools, like our own, seek, as they should, to deal with the "normal" youth. Most schoolmasters recognize their lack of qualification to cure the seriously disturbed young person, and the need of any such youth to be in a group smaller than is commonly practical in any but a school for "exceptional children." There is still great need for more such schools to provide continuing professional psychotherapy. Until this is accomplished, and public acceptance of these schools is general, the school for the "normal" youth must increasingly seek the help of the consulting psychiatrist and must study with greatest care to improve its own mental health program. Fortunately, there are presently available far more excellent sources for study and guidance on this topic than most school people have yet utilized.[2]

While the public school system must work out its own salvation within the framework of "education for all," the independent school has, in the power of selection of students, an invaluable instrument for cultivation of mental health within the student body. Properly exercised, this should prevent most of the damaging failure, dismissal and disgrace that occur far too often in our schools. The careful investigation of applicants can also be the means of gathering information which will avert later complications and greatly advance development of each student into an emotionally strong and healthy adult.

Dr. Gallagher writes: "An adolescent is the product of his past. Since no two have the same heredity or are exposed to the same environmental factors, there is little wonder that each is unique, an individual whose attributes and needs differ from others. Not only is the number of gene combinations which go to form one's inheritance infinite, but so also is the variety of environmental influences" (20, p. 4). The first need of the schoolmaster is to know much of the essential nature of the individual and all that is possible about his "environmental influences" and past history.

There can be no substitute for "individual attention" either in the preliminary study of a youth, or his later guidance (40). It is, however, accepted that group therapy, in expert hands, can mitigate the lack of it, where time and staff may necessarily be inadequate. Where the opportunity and the philosophy of a school place no obvious limits on "individual attention"—it is still important that it be given subtly, so that the student is encouraged to ever greater inner se-

[2] Many bibliographies are available. Especially we can recommend the Educational Policy Committee of the National Council of Independent Schools, 84 State Street, Boston, Mass., as a valuable source of material useful to the schoolmaster.

curity and independence, and weaned from "attention seek-ing." This requires infinite watchfulness by parents and teachers.

Inner Life

Yet, as we become more alert and discriminating in our detection of possible illness, we would do well to re-read the excellent article by Dr. P. Rube on "The Inner World of Adolescence" to recheck our own ideas of normality in this period.

We do not think that most adolescents are neurotic, for we do not think that most families are disturbed. We do believe that neurosis is a pathological condition which still is the privilege of the minority.

When, in adolescents, we deal with reactions of aggressiveness, withdrawal, anger, affection, sympathy, exasperation, love, repulsion, rebellion, submission, and others, we do not believe that we are dealing with pathological reactions *unless* these reactions are part of a morbid pattern. Even though many of these reactions may be disagreeable to some, who find them excessive or unpleasant, they may not be connected with any underlying morbid condition. The neurotic attitudes or reactions are not those which are unexpected or inexplainable. We also must discriminate between reactions and attitudes which are amenable to re-education and those which require psychotherapy, based on a psychiatric approach . . .

There are as many human "normalities" as there are *undamaged* individuals . . .

We think that if adolescents are able to conform to their environment, they may be considered as normal. But we also believe that there are adolescents who cannot conform to their environment, because this environment is abnormal, and, because they are normal. In both cases, their attitudes—while contradictory at the level of statistical and ideal normality—are justified and "normal" at the level of "individual functioning."

There is a time when the adolescent has not yet been

integrated into the community of adults, but has already left the community of children. Here he stands alone, with his store of drives more or less confusedly transformed into wishes, with hopes and desires which make him an individual unknown not only to others but also to himself. At that point, very often, the adolescents would say that they feel as if their personality had become "diffused," and some of them even become aware of the continuous effort they sustain in order to preserve a feeling of inner unity . . .

The second consequence is that most of the nervous energy of the young individual used by his imaginary structures cannot be directed toward his studies. This explains two facts commonly observed in adolescents: (1) Some present a progressive lowering, or a sudden decline, of their school marks; they fail in their tests, without any apparent reason. This episode may be dramatic enough to alarm their teachers, their parents and themselves. If the recovery does not occur soon enough, because too often inadequate steps are taken by the environment, it may subsequently lead them to many complex reactions. Usually the adolescent recovers after a few months and is then able to resume his studies normally. (2) Other adolescents are able to "save face" and to maintain their previous rank in their class. They are capable of passing their tests successfully. But were their knowledge examined later on, it would be found that they had previously undergone a period when practically nothing was retained from their studies. For that reason, so many individuals are obliged, later, to study again some of the subjects they had supposedly learned during their adolescence, studies they cannot utilize at the time of their adulthood, when they need them most . . .

The increase of physical sensations may be so strong and so sudden that the young individual feels as though he were discovering the external world for the first time. Nevertheless, the newly acquired sharpness of his perception may not help him to establish a closer contact with reality. On the contrary, his new physical hypersensitiveness may be transferred to his inner world. Since the latter is not charged with cumbersome details and useless shadows, it will appear so vivid and so full of relief, that the real world will appear flat, colorless and unattractive. This contrast may increase so much that the external world fades away, and the adolescent may temporarily lose contact with reality. That explains why some periods of adolescence may resemble a pre-psychotic, or even a confirmed psychotic process which is distinct enough to worry the environment. However, in most adolescents there is an alternation between daydreaming and reality, and it is finally the daydream which fades away, and reality which wins . . .

Many temporary disturbances observed in adolescents are related to the rapid and striking changes brought to the image of one's self at that period. That important subject definitely deserves further studies . . .

The most mature and healthiest adolescent reacts with a healthy aggressiveness, the first manifestation of which often is some hyperactivity which helps him to overcome his anxiety and heal his wound . . .

All our lives long, we act not only according to the demands of our ego—stimulated by our instincts and controlled by our superego—but also according to the demands of our inner image of ourselves, which follows its own particular laws and patterns. In all instances of our existence, we are accompanied by the ghost we have created, housed and fed with our dreams [45, pp. 673-691].

The Selection of Students

Testing and Placement

In adolescence more than any other period, the individual is a creature of the group. He must belong, he must succeed meeting its demands. Obviously he should not be accepted into a group situation where he does not have a reasonable chance for success. Failure despite effort will warp him. His resulting conflicts may have a disturbing influence on the less stable of his companions. Thus the desire to help the individual has often led the understanding schoolmaster into unrealistic optimism harmful to both the individual and the group.

Independent schools are usually charged with preparing students for higher education. They must use intelligence tests as a primary instrument of selection. In common use are such verbal tests as the Kuhlmann-Anderson, Otis, and California Mental Maturity. Stressing verbal factors, they measure from an early age the qualities most demanded by colleges today, verbal facility and reasoning—as well as mathematical aptitudes tested on a verbal level. Independent school percentiles are available.[3] Many schools keep their own percentiles through the years to check on prognostication of success in a particular school or college environment. Increasing are the use of the Junior Scholastic Aptitude Test of the Secondary Education Board, the American Council Psychological Examination, and, still more recently, the School and College Abilities Test of the Educational Testing Service. All are designed for administration as group tests— thus their accuracy is subject to the usual reservations regarding time and setting of administration, skill of administration, and emotional factors momentarily affecting any individual being tested. The three latter tests are "power tests" of presently functioning ability, in terms of percentiles —although "I.Q." equivalents are available.[4] In the use of all of these tests, the obvious caution should be repeated that they will probably fail to measure at all accurately the capacity of a boy or girl who has experienced difficulty or delay in language skill acquisition or who has an emotional block to specific phases of learning.

It is also well to remember that the three first tests were standardized on the general population, so that I.Q. figures may be relatively high, and that such terms as "average" and "superior" have little or no meaning for the student seeking

3 Educational Records Bureau, 21 Audubon Avenue, New York 32, N.Y.
4 Educational Records Bureau, 21 Audubon Avenue, New York 32, N.Y.

a college education today. Currently, only those in the "high average," "superior," and "gifted," classifications will even be given the chance to compete.[5]

As group tests can be such gross and varying measures of an individual (many schoolmasters could point out increase or loss of from 10 to 20 percentile points in a twelve-month period), it is important to have, as nearly as possible, a youth's I.Q. history over several years before admission. Not only is this fairer to the student, but extreme variations may point to emotional factors important to know.

If it is possible to administer an intelligence test individually, the Wechsler-Bellevue Test appears to be the most effective current instrument for those twelve and over. We likewise find the Wechsler Intelligence Scale for Children the most satisfactory one for those below twelve, although not yet as satisfactory as the adult and youth forms. Dr. Wechsler's concept of intelligence is increasingly accepted as a better measure of over-all potential than the purely verbal test. Certainly it does give more weight to the "g" and "x" factors. As Dr. Wechsler himself has pointed out in his excellent introduction to the test (58) there are many reasons to believe that later tests and revisions of his present test will prove still more effective.

There is difference of opinion as to the value of the separate subtest scores in studying a youth's abilities, or in diagnosing his problems. Many competent psychologists believe in considering only the major divisions—verbal I.Q. and performance I.Q.—as the truly significant factors. Our experi-

[5] As this is being written, most independent colleges seek an I.Q. of 120 or higher, and set a "floor" of 115. These figures appear likely to rise in the overcrowded years immediately ahead for our secondary schools and colleges.

Such extreme selectivity may or may not be defensible, or even moral in a democracy, but it exists so universally that it must be faced. Very serious is the lack of a group test for the "g" factor, or "x" factor. Most schools and colleges still pridefully point to the rare acceptance of an average or moderate I.Q. student whose record had attested high motivations and character—but he is increasingly difficult to find in the halls of higher learning today.

ence has led us to be hopeful of results that can be obtained from understanding use of the subtest scores. We have found it constructive to convert the raw score of these tests into I.Q. equivalents for practical use by teachers studying a boy's aptitudes, handicaps or emotional obstacles.

Our school pays especial attention to the digit span and digit symbol tests as potential indicators of anxiety. If both of these yield unusually low scores, we count them good indication for further psychiatric examination. A low digit span score also usually reflects in a low arithmetic score and may give a key to improvement in mathematical performance by the removal of anxiety, and the advisability of repeated drill to establish security in fundamentals. The picture arrangement and picture completion tests certainly give valuable clues to social attitudes and adaptations. These may also point out the superficially bright individual, who may yet appear clearly inferior on such tests of reasoning as the similarities section. On rare occasions when the object assembly tests are failed, we have found it evidence of grave disturbance.

Objective achievement tests, such as the Stanford, Metropolitan, Iowa, or California, and a great variety of improved and diagnostic reading tests are in general use in both public and independent schools. Thus it is not difficult to secure a picture of a youth's learning history. The achievement tests, however, are too often given in groups that are too large, or by teachers unskilled in test administration. Thus the school that can give its own to an applicant, or be sure that it is done by a trained and competent examiner, is wise. Obviously, class and section placement of the applicant should result from careful use of both intelligence and achievement scores. Vital to the student's mental growth and to his emotional stability is a firm realism on this score. Emotionally, it is equally vital that the superior student be placed in superior competition, with skilled teaching designed to stimulate the gifted. The need of the able student with language disability or other evident handicap to receive the support of expert special training, either individually or in very small groups, is axiomatic if severe frustration is to be avoided.

Personality Descriptions

Experience has led us to distrust the personality rating scales, now in common use, as cumbersome and less revealing than the essay type of description. The usual public school report card is likewise often inadequate.

Once a trustworthy test record and educational history is obtained, the schoolmaster will need a further description of his future student's home background, social characteristics, other interests and abilities, temperament, and character. These should come from the previous principal and teachers, and whatever other reliable sources are available. Evaluating such letters is difficult, but in addition to whatever may be known about the writer, his perception and standards, such letters inevitably are self-revealing to the careful reader.

Personality Tests

There are "personality inventories" which can be fairly accurate and useful. As their administration consumes considerable time, these are likely to be more valuable for later guidance and counseling than for selection of new students.

The Science Research Associates Junior Inventory for Grades IV-VIII, and the S. R. A. Youth Inventory for Grades VII-XII have proved their value over a number of years. Three newer tests for the high school age—the Kuder Preference Record-Personal, the Guilford-Zimmerman Temperament Survey and the Heston Personal Adjustment Inventory —are favorably regarded by competent authority.[6]

6 For further information on these and similar tests, refer to Educational Records Bureau, 21 Audubon Avenue, New York 32, N.Y.

It appears that there still is need of some short test or other quick screening device which could be administered to applicants for admission to our schools, both to describe general personality and to detect existent or incipient emotional disturbance. Some schools use the House-Tree-Persons Test or other picture drawing techniques with relative success. They are usually more revealing with children than with self-conscious and reticent adolescents.

A projective test which may prove valuable in both research and later counseling of both youth and teachers is the Adult-Child Interaction Test.[7]

The Parent Interview and Parental Attitudes

For personality evaluation, we find that the interview with the parent and the student yields the most satisfactory information. The interview is conducted in a dynamic way so that it often reveals even more about home and parents than about the boy himself.

Parents usually volunteer the child's educational and developmental history, but careful queries may be needed. Still more important is the family constellation and the parents' interpretation of the youngster's part in it.

Often family members accompany the candidate to the interview. Informal observation of and conversation with the family group can tell much. Sometimes the absence of one parent or the other is significant. Parents will usually talk freely about grandparents, and vice versa. The spoiling grandparent seems to be less common than in days gone by, and in the families of many overbusy or overanxious parents, we find that it has been grandparents, aunt, or uncle who have provided most of a youth's security, often with great common sense and true affection. If the schoolmaster can know them, he will find real allies.

[7] Presented by Theron Alexander in *Child Development Publications,* 1341 Euclid, University of Illinois, Champaign, Ill.

Siblings, or perhaps the lack of them, are such powerful factors in personality formation that an opportunity for observation can be invaluable. Parents will usually talk very freely about all their children and their interrelationships. The interviewer will evaluate the objectivity of the parents' description, ever watchful for signs of favoritism or prejudice. Parental differences and conflicts often come into the open in these discussions. Simultaneous interview with both parents, if feasible, is not only the most revealing, but invaluable in securing family understanding of the school's function and their future cooperation in guidance.

The problem parent usually reveals himself in the interview. Overanxiety, perfectionism, rejection are not easily concealed. One needs to be guarded about the parent who says to the schoolmaster: "I leave him in your hands, you have had so much more experience than I, and this is your business." Sometimes this is true humility; more often a subconscious rejection causes the desire to pass parental responsibilities on to the school. In such situations we are prone to remind the parents of their responsibility; that we are simply a new and expanded environment for their boy; that our function is the furthering of earlier home training in closest cooperation with the family, and that we will expect their frequent visits and close contact through correspondence.

More common, however, are guilt feelings on the part of one or both parents over the youngster's leaving home. Many parents report that neighbors and friends think them unfeeling to "send Johnny away." Reassurance of the school's personal interest, close contact, and concern to maintain home ties usually settles this. If doubt and guilt persist, beware real rejection!

It's an all-too-common idea that the child who goes to boarding school before the high school years does so either because of scholastic difficulties, a broken home, or a behavior problem. A series of careful studies made of our own student population leads me to take sharp issue with this assumption. If the boarding school takes the stand that it exists to stimulate and enlarge the scope of youngsters of normal background and development, and superior ability, it need not be flooded with "problem children."

Elsewhere in this book a statement is made that more than half of the students who appear in the psychiatrist's office for therapy come from broken homes. Perhaps this is one of the most common sources of adolescent illness. From the schoolmaster's point of view, however, I believe that divorce need not be a severely upsetting factor. What is important are the factors which brought about the divorce and the way in which they were handled. Many boarding schools, from my observation, deal with no greater proportion of children from divorced homes than does the suburban day school; in our own experience, the number is between 10 and 14 per cent of the total student population. Attitudes toward divorce have become far more tolerant and sensible. Most thoughtful parents, however bitter their own maladjustments, are cautious about involving their children in a tug of war or of using them as pawns. Frequently the schoolmaster can help them.

We feel that the memory of conflict resolved by frank separation is much less damaging to the child than the subjection to a continuingly unhappy home. Some trauma from divorce is inevitable, but parental love can minimize it. Children who have been in a home of conflict have made self-protective adaptations already and may have considerable toughness and resilience. In general, they experience relief, satisfaction and hopefulness at the clear-cut resolution of the parental conflict and the establishment of a program which enables them to pursue their own lives and goals.

Perhaps the hardest bit of realism for a parent to accept is the intellectual limitations of his child. Ego and ambition dictate that even if he is not "Harvard material," he is certainly "average," which is taken to mean a "perfectly good candidate for any small college." Commonly a parent will assume that social facility or mechanical aptitude in a son are indications of "brightness" that should be reflected in school work regardless of his verbal aptitude. The facts of today's competition for higher education are still not fully realized by many. Although the emotional acceptance of individual intelligence variations is becoming more general, yet parents' desire to see a son or daughter emulate them, or succeed where they have failed, remain very powerful. This desire can be, for the child, a very dislocating force. There is a great need for independent secondary schools that are less competitive and for junior colleges to serve the youngster of fine character and average ability.

Encouraging is the fact that the popularity of extreme permissiveness is on the wane. Parents remark on the value of discipline and the security gained from guidance, firm opinion, and example.

Unfortunately, we rarely find a parent volunteering any information about a youngster's sex life and experience, or the normalcy of his attitudes. To state that he is not yet interested in girls, or has always had normal attitudes toward them, is just about as far as any parent cares to go without prodding. Even on inquiry, few appear to know anything about their youngsters' thinking or feeling; many too little about the extent of their maturation. If the youngster's social adjustment and anxieties or other indicative signs lead the interviewer to suspect that he has concerns in this area, the parent will usually comment briefly that reproduction has been discussed, or insist that a very open, confident family attitude has prevailed in dealing with the whole subject of sex. Far too rarely has this really been true.

Our Supplementary Information Blank carries a very open question: "What does your son know about the facts of reproduction?" Writing the answer, even in a few lines, saves the parent embarrassment and often gives revealing information as to attitudes if not as to facts. The prize reply came from a grandmother who, substituting for her daughter in filling out the blank, wrote "will bear watching"!

Time is never adequate in a personal interview with the parents, but when handled patiently and sympathetically, an hour of advance discussion can be worth weeks and months of struggling blindly with a youngster's unforeseen problem. On rare occasions, a personal interview with applicants and parents, either at the school, which is preferable for the student, or in their home, which can be most revealing, is impossible. At such times school and personal references become overwhelmingly important and the perceptiveness and integrity of the reference is paramount. A questionnaire sent to the parents is most useful in these cases. It is also a valuable supplement to the personal interview.

The Student Interview

In our school, we customarily interview parents first, apart from the applicant, in order to give them the opportunity to unburden themselves unreservedly and to establish mutual understanding, as well as background for the student interview. During the same time another teacher or selected student will befriend the applicant and show him the school. This provides excellent opportunity for observation, a good chance for the boy to relax, and an unhurried introduction to a friendly environment designed for enjoyment as well as work.

The student's interview, following the parents', can usually be much briefer, though covering similar territory. Usually the applicant, except the very self-absorbed one, is capable of concise answers and can relax easily with a friendly interviewer's attention strongly focused upon him. The parent interview or previous school record will have provided information of hobby or special interest adequate for establishing rapport. We conduct the interview on a totally nonauthoritarian basis, inquiring primarily about likes, dislikes, interests, successes and failures, without any judgmental expressions. Whether the child has been realistically described by his parents soon becomes evident. If not, a much longer interview will probably be needed, stimulating freedom for self-expression, and omitting reference to the parental comments.

Piecing together the youngster's remarks about himself, his siblings, his friends and activities, and the background of the parent interview, we can learn much about his personality, and uncover disturbances, if they exist. Encouraged, he will usually talk freely about his school subjects or learning difficulties.

Later in the interview, questioning about vocational ambition will also yield valuable material, such as the degree of identification with the father, possible fears of intellectual limitations, domination by family example or tradition, feeling of economic security or insecurity, and social attitudes. Another helpful query we commonly use is: "What would you do if you had three to six months in which you were free to do anything you please, go anywhere in the world, and spend whatever money is necessary to satisfy yourself that you have done exactly what you want at this present time?" The range of answers is, of course, as wide as one's imagination. The youngster in difficulty in school or worried about his intellectual progress frequently replies timidly that he would study all that time as hard as he can. Others would join the Brooklyn Dodgers as bat boy, work in a guided missile experimental laboratory, or camp and hunt alone in the woods. These open-ended questions regarding long-range goals and the immediate desires form a sort of verbal projective test. The manner of reply is as fascinating and revealing as the content.

The relationship between father and son, and the degree of identification, usually comes out clearly in response to the vocational query. It is, of course, important to determine the boy's self-concept, long-range goals or their lack, the amount of confidence he manifests in his own capabilities, and his tendency to enter or to avoid competition. Also especially valuable is the opportunity to inquire about his father, his father's interests and activities—important background which the father seldom volunteers. Reticence regarding personalities, parents, siblings, teachers, others, may require delicate handling to elicit their significance.

The second question about immediate use of free time quickly reveals anxiety, escape or fantasy, parental attitudes toward freedom, financial anxiety, and so on. Although specifically directed away from it, it is also likely to give a good idea of the student's attitudes toward school work, his enjoyment of or frustration in it, and his appreciation of its purposefulness in relation to his own life.

Discussion with the student in this opening interview can be of infinite value in the establishment of rapport, release of tensions, building of confidence and, in many other ways, setting the stage for a successful school experience. Often times we find it helpful to suggest that during the continuing months before entering school the student write us further about his interests and activities, and the success he is having in handling any problems he may encounter. "Out of sight, out of mind" is often the reaction to this, and a very healthy one, too. However, usually a sufficient rapport has been established so that a friendly note from us will bring a fairly full, confident and chatty reply.

The interview with the student is usually followed immediately by another one with the parents, hopefully brief. Sometimes, if the student himself is suspicious of adult collusion, it is better to have him sit in too. The conclusion should inspire mutual confidence and cooperation. In rare cases, an interview may end up in a suggestion for a psychiatric interview and guidance, particularly in those situations where adolescent rebellion is excessive, or parental anxiety and tension too great to be easily released by the layman. On occasion, some mild therapy can greatly improve the adaptation to the school environment; or perhaps, it will be the psychiatrist alone that is needed—not the school. Frankness on this score is surely the schoolmaster's duty.

Once the school has secured all readily available information about the student, his family relations, his general background of experience, and his emotional growth, action can be taken on the application. It is, we feel strongly, the school's obligation to accept only those students whose emotional development, as far as it can be ascertained, falls within the degree of normality that the school is realistically equipped to handle. Undue optimism is no favor to boy or school. Yet frequently a child will be something of a problem at home, have conflicts with one parent or the other, or feel tensions with his siblings, yet be capable of good adjustment with his peers in a school environment. In fact, many students need the opportunity for nearly constant contemporary companionship, and the socializing experience which the boarding school, if wisely administered, can provide.

A School Program for Mental Health

Once the school has selected a group of emotionally healthy students, its responsibility for the continuing maintenance of an alert and dynamic mental health program is obvious. Much study has been given this subject, and so much written about it that this chapter should only list a few cardinal points.

1. Maintenance of a confident, friendly spirit between student and teacher.

2. Maintenance of close, frank, and cooperative relationship between parents and school.

3. Painstaking class and section placement so that each student's academic task is such that he can achieve with satisfaction, yet be continually stimulated to growth. This will require flexibility, gifted and devoted teaching, and an imaginative curriculum. Groups should be small where possible.

4. A good health and physical education program to develop competence and courage.

5. A wide range of extracurricular activities which will encourage special talents and provide emotional outlets.

6. An atmosphere of purposefulness pursued with happy companionship and humor.

7. Cultivation of as much student responsibility and self-government as the maturity of the group permits.

8. Judicious use of praise and confident, consistent firmness by the adults.

9. Sufficient attention to and awareness of the outer world and its problems to stimulate his search for long-range goals.

10. Opportunity for intelligent religious instruction, discussion and worship to encourage faith and service.

Oh for the perfect school and the ideal teacher!

It is important that there be some group instruction in sex education, preferably tied in with science, yet, let me repeat my earnest plea that parents consider sex education their own primary responsibility. The school or pediatrician may provide information, but cannot give emotional content to the subject, without which it is relatively meaningless and detached, often unwholesome. It is likewise important that the science courses include instruction in personal health and hygiene and in the basic principles of mental health. A youth's understanding of his own emotional growth should no more remain obscure to him than that of his physical development. Only thus can he interpret and integrate the experience of everyday living.

AUTHORITY AND THE ADOLESCENT

It is almost axiomatic in our culture that many adolescents suffer from overauthoritarianism in the home. Many is the father, and not too infrequent the mother, who unconsciously assumes a dogmatic or perfectionist attitude. With this youth, the schoolmaster will do well to heed Gesell, Ilg and Ames: "Parent-youth relationships often suffer severe strain, but they may take on a significant meaning when viewed in the light of their developmental implications. This does not mean that an emotional episode should be judged or indulged on the basis of a distant past or a remote future . . . In developmental guidance the immediate present has priority. The task is to recognize the growth forces which may reveal themselves in subtle, quiet signs or in dramatic manifestations of self-assertion, of confession, contrition, resistance, pride, and in other forms of counter thrust. *Authoritarian discipline ignores the significance of growth*" (21, p. 385).

The adolescent, to achieve the security of his own independence and adulthood, must rebel against unreasonable authority, and occasionally even against *all* authority. It is therefore exceedingly vital that the teacher who exercises the functions of parent substitute or therapeutic counselor have a clear picture of the youth's past experience with authority, and his reaction to it. It is possible, particularly in formal schooling situations, for a teacher to find that a boy has endowed him with so much authority as to make their personal relationship difficult. The teacher needs to know the degree of authority exercised by the previous father figure and by the previous school environment, if he is to help his student to a healthy concept. The teacher must, in other cases, be willing to accept, for a time at least, a possible unreasonable rebellion against him as the authority symbol, if the child has already established a need to flaunt authority in his own home or previous environment.

For the disturbed lad, it is especially important not to permit evident relaxing of the general authority of the school, nor to appear to side with the individual against his social milieu and those responsible for its direction. Understanding interpretation to both will usually win out. Where possible, conflict is best handled by placing the rebellious youngster —as well as the one who feels insignificant in relation to his peers—in a position of as substantial responsibility as he can effectively carry. Thus he himself may experience the exercise of authority as a means of resolving his own conflicts with it.

The ultimate symbol of authority in the school—the headmaster or headmistress—may experience difficulty in securing the rapport necessary for counseling a youth. The transfer of authority from parent to the headmaster is so direct, and the power which the headmaster can exercise over the student and his life may *seem* to be so absolute, as to make the development of mutual confidence and emphatic relationship difficult. Clearly, however, no one will stay long at the head of a school who cannot solve this problem! Most schoolmasters and schoolmistresses are well equipped for the modest, restrained, resourceful, and delicate exercise of their parent-substitute function. Those not so qualified are familiar in fact and fiction and, for mental health reasons, should be promptly encouraged to resign from the profession.

THE ADVISOR

Every youth should have, either in his chief classroom teacher, his housemaster, or an advisor assigned to him, a counselor in matters academic. This counselor will, hopefully, be chosen as one who has true understanding and sympathy for the problems of his age level, and for any learning difficulties the particular youth may face. Hopefully, too, he may be the person to whom the close emotional guidance of the boy or girl can be delegated. The selection of the advisor is vitally important. Yet just as one psychotherapist will succeed in establishing rapport where another may not, so the arbitrary assignments of teaching advisors are bound to have their flaws, no matter how carefully planned. If the advisor can be appointed apparently for scholastic reasons, a wise teacher will encourage the development of an empathic relationship naturally, and without self-consciousness on the part of the advisee.

Clearly the advisor should be supplied with all pertinent information regarding educational history, family background, emotional maturity, physical strengths and handicaps, and special talents and interests. He should be informed about the family constellation and, as far as known, its significance to the boy. He should demonstrate to the boy that this assignment is one which he, the advisor, enjoys, or has requested, and that he is ready and eager to serve as friend. There will be many students who will need a very intimate type of support; others who will wish to feel quite independent, yet glad to have someone in the background to whom they may turn in times of strain or trouble. In due time, it should be established that the advisor's concern is individual, even above the standards and goals of the school. Yet he should not at any time assume with his advisee a negative or antagonistic attitude toward school administration or rules. They are essentials of the environment to be accepted for wholesome adaptation. He should know the advisee's physical history and, especially in the case of the adolescent, the degree of his physical and sexual maturity, which can be secured from the medical department in the form of a Greulich rating. This information will prepare him for some of the emotional concerns or worries which may develop naturally as the youngster passes through succeeding periods of physical and emotional growth. He should have such a relationship with his advisee that quips and pranks, the normal effervescence of youth, can be discussed frankly, without fear that the boy's confidences will be revealed. Confidences should not come into the realm of discipline, unless their significance is socially serious or deeply morbid. The advisor should be the substitute father, or the lay therapist, if either is needed.

At the same time, he should consider it his responsibility to interpret his adolescent advisee to other faculty members and to keep the school administrators and authorities well informed regarding the youngster's progress. He should establish a personal relationship with the parents and consider it his responsibility to keep understanding contact with them. If he is the kind of person with whom the student can establish a degree of identification, this will be especially wholesome for those who do not yet have an adequate father identification. Frequently, also, the advisor can interest contemporaries or slightly older students in the guidance and comfort of a confused youth. The advisor should also be quick to report to higher authority any difficulties with his advisee, or any lack of rapport, after he has made a sincere effort to secure it. At this point a change of advisor, skillfully maneuvered, is probably in order.

Spotting the Need for Professional Help

Despite all the hominess that a school can simulate, all the friendliness that it can generate, and all the security that it can represent—there will still be those youngsters whose inner life is incomplete, or in turmoil, and who should have more expert guidance than even the most thoughtful teacher is able to provide. Some will need, as may their parents, help from a professional specialist in the resolution of inter-family or inner conflicts, or in environmental adaptation. We have already remarked upon uses of the Wechsler-

Bellevue test to spot individuals with actual or incipient emotional problems. Observation of behavior may be more important. Although experience has led us to look for obvious symptoms, behavior irregularities or deviation are often difficult to classify. Each disturbed youngster is so different, and such a variety of forces have been affecting him, that he will inevitably present a combination of symptoms observable in varying degrees. The illustrative examples which follow may serve to guide the layman's recognition of symptoms which are frequently predominant.[8]

Working Too Hard

An easily identifiable individual is the youngster whose established capacity and habitual performance are at wide variance. If the ability, carefully and repeatedly tested, is far below the performance, the teacher knows that the effort involved is costing the individual heavily in emotional energy. This may be producing inner conflicts, or may interfere seriously with the youngster's breadth of interest and activity, and his social development. Many times it may be emotionally important to him that he and his parents accept more modest goals, or that the school reduce the academic burden to bring in diversionary activities which coincide with his interests and provide him emotional outlets. Often this can be done effectively without help from the psychiatrist.

Jim, the eldest of three children, in a happy, sociable family, was attractive and friendly. Jim enjoyed his sports and was well adjusted socially, but had never been much of a success in school. The family attributed his difficulties to frequent school changes as they moved about during the war and for business reasons. In his relations with contemporaries

8 These examples cannot be complete "case histories" in the usual medical sense, but do include accurate data which, to this writer, seem pertinent. All names have been changed, and in two cases other minor items also, in order to preserve the subject's anonymity.

and adults he gave a superficial appearance of intelligence, although the careful observer would notice that his vocabulary was rather simple. When he was admited to boarding school at the age of twelve, his intelligence tested at average level, and his history showed retardation in reading and spelling. Previous expert tutoring had produced relatively little progress—and had finally aroused his strong resentment over the demands upon him.

The new school, continuing the tutoring under a very skilled and understanding teacher, came to feel that it had located the difficulty in his eyesight. They recommended another eye specialist's examination, which disclosed aniseikonia and fairly severe fusion difficulty. Corrective lenses were provided and eye exercises carried out faithfully. The boy felt that his reading and language troubles, about which he had begun to worry considerably, were soon to melt away. He wore his glasses pridefully and commented repeatedly on how much better he could read.

As a result of the attention, training and correction, his reading, spelling and mathematics test scores improved. His teachers began to feel some ray of hope. In the adjustment to his new school, he had been realistically placed in a group with whom he was on an achievement par, although his I.Q. score was well below the group average. Increasingly teachers remarked upon his mental slowness and his apparent weakness both in retention and in reasoning power. Inquiry was made into the possibility of brain damage, either at birth or later—with negative results.

More and more Jim showed strain under the effort to keep up with his work and his classmates. At this point a second Bellevue-Wechsler test confirmed the growing conviction of the school that he was a boy of clearly limited ability and that his program must be arranged accordingly. His picture arrangement and picture completion scores were among his best, explaining his superficial social alertness. The anxiety scores were relatively normal, but comprehension and reasoning were alarmingly low.

The battery of emotional tests showed normal reality acceptance and personality organization—as well as confirming the Wechsler's evidence of limited ability. Constraint was evident, due to the incompatability of capacity and goal.

The parents, confronted with the evidence, accepted it, gave up the aim of ultimate college preparation, agreed to the repeating of his grade, and to later transfer to a less demanding school that would emphasize manual arts and vocational training. This essentially stable boy, glad to be released from unrealistic demands, also accepts the new program happily.

Can't read—can't spell

Much has been written regarding the effect of language difficulties, particularly reading and spelling handicaps. These, thank fortune, are receiving a more adequate share of attention in the school world of today. The origin may be physical, a sight or hearing deficiency; neurological, due to training elements, including unsuitable teaching methods; or psychological. Whatever the cause, when "Johnnie can't read" the schoolmaster can well assume that there has been a considerable emotional effect. Any conscientious teacher will bear this in mind as he applies the recognized cures. Rarely, we feel, will psychiatric help be needed to overcome the learning problem itself. It is, however, vital to remember that other disturbances, themselves needing psychological attention, are frequently accompanied by language difficulty. In extreme cases of prolonged disability, there may have been severe enough trauma to warrant the aid of a mild psychiatric boost to the remedial teacher's efforts.

Ben was twelve, but could scarcely read third grade words, and had absolutely no number concept. After years of school failure, he was convinced that he was practically a moron, and his indifference and discouragement were pathetic. A year in a military school had through its drill and the uniform given him some confidence, but only deepened his sense of academic inadequacy. Now in a new school three years later, his language skills have advanced eight grades, and his mathematical abilities are of eighth grade level— the final emotional block overcome. An I.Q. in the high seventies is now replaced by a Wechsler-Bellevue Full Scale of 107, subdivided as follows: Verbal Scale I.Q. 110; Performance Scale I.Q. 103.

In accepting Ben, the boarding school saw enough beyond the apparent intellectual limitations to gamble at least on a trial. Skillful tutoring and encouragement gradually won his cooperation. His long-denied success began to come to him, through help continued summer as well as winter. He developed single-minded determination which will probably yet carry him much further. Illuminating is the fact that he still displays very low scores on digit span and digit symbol tests which will probably rise as his anxiety continues to lessen.

Bill, age eleven, is the son of immigrant parents who spoke a European language in the home. Father, outstandingly successful himself, had been delighted with the older brother's progress after being transferred from a weak school in an industrial town to a small boarding school. When Bill was first tested by the WISC he scored 88 on the verbal I.Q. and 153 on the performance section! The latter was so extremely high that despite the verbal weakness, his potential was given further careful consideration. This developed the fact that in his third, fourth and fifth grades he had been in classes of seventy or more children, just at the most critical period of language development. In a single year of small class instruction, with considerable individual help, he has made better than double normal achievement and gain in verbal skills which may well be the key to salvaging a technical mind of outstanding future value.

Ted's problem, however, complicated as it was by many factors, did not have as happy an outcome. He was a twin, whose slightly more able brother was favored in the home, producing very complicated sibling rivalry. His early day school did not recognize—nor attempt to correct—his reading difficulties. Energetic and eager for love and attention, he found his father stiff, distant, unsympathetic—preoccupied with his own rather superficial portion of adult life. The youngster was literally "sent away" to boarding school, at the age of eleven, a retarded child who felt his rejection keenly, although he couldn't express his feelings verbally.

He had a chip on his shoulder, an eagerness for status and attention which was constantly expressed in aggressive manifestations, quarrelsomeness, bullying and endless mischief. The school worked hard to help him. He was given remedial language training, much outlet in sports and crafts, and great patience and encouragement. The mother sought to understand and help, but was both too busy, and too confused by the problem to have any deep effect. Academic progress was slow because of intellectual limitations that couldn't be changed. At different times, two teachers undertook to establish a substitute father relationship, but each time Ted's compulsive aggression terminated the proffered support. In preadolescence there appeared an absorption in sex which developed rapidly and insistently in the direction of homosexuality. Ted began to display sadistic tendencies. Although psychiatric advice had earlier been sought by the school, the parents had rejected such help. Finally Ted became so clearly a sick boy that he had to be withdrawn from school to a psychiatrist's care and later institutionalization. With a growing understanding from the parents, who have sought psychiatric help themselves, and their acceptance of Ted's limitations, he will probably yet find his reasonable place in society.

Immature

Certainly the obviously immature boy needs watching and study, although psychotherapy may not be indicated. Physical causes are common—likewise overprotection, either in the very early years or later. Commonly this type of lad needs encouragement, friendship, and gradual new experience in normal developmental sequence. Usually it is sound to place a boy with characteristics of immaturity with the age group in which he is then on a par. He may make more rapid progress than his classmates, and eventually achieve acceptance and success on his own age level.

Sometimes we meet an immature boy who needs psychotherapy. Overprotection, both by parents and much older siblings, may have so reduced drive and motivation as to seriously weaken competitive strivings and the growth of the self. Guidance to parents can be very important in this type of situation. Other adolescents who may be immature or retarded physically may be so aware of the gap between age and size to require encouragement and reassurance beyond that easily within the scope of the layman. This is not infrequently the case in a boy or girl whose sex maturity is delayed considerably beyond that of his contemporaries.

Joe was a premature child, born before the seventh-month period. Both father and mother were very small of stature, and the baby truly tiny. Saving the mother at the birth, and keeping the baby alive in his first few months were momentous struggles, finaly won with the help of able medical care and devoted maternal grandparents. Within two years it became apparent that the war marriage was a mis-match, and divorce ensued. The mother found it necessary to go to work as the father's support and interest dwindled and disappeared. Much of the little boy's care fell to the grandparents.

Many factors combined to retard the youngster's growth and development. Premature birth had accentuated the effects of inherited physical frailty. Grandparents combined anxious protection with perfectionist demands and training. Mother sought independence for herself. In concern lest the grandparents spoil him, she rationed her own attention and love to him sparingly. His academic progress in public school was slow—from the beginning much complicated by reading and spelling difficulties.

At the age of nine, he was placed in boarding school, both to overcome academic difficulties and to remove him from the overattention of the grandparents. By this time, it had become clearly evident that grandparental pampering was hindering his emotional growth—which had progressed little further than that of the normal six-year-old.

The school proved effective, and Joe gradually overcame most of his academic difficulties. Recognizing his natural immaturity, school and parents had agreed to his placement in a group from one to two years younger than himself. In this setting, despite a slow start, he throve in the competition and matured encouragingly. Despite his tiny stature, he became an able baseball player—and so improved his emotional and social relationships that he was chosen and performed well as head of the younger boys' student government.

Joe's development was greatly accelerated when, about his twelfth birthday, his mother remarried, bringing into the family circle a most understanding, interested, and companionable stepfather. A year later, Joe was faced with the loss of his much-adored grandfather, and accepted it in remarkably good fashion. Soon thereafter a small stepbrother was born, an incident which, a couple of years earlier, would have been very upsetting to him. By this time, he was able to welcome the newcomer with secure pride and adoring affection.

Only a few months later he faced another difficult test. He had thus far been able to maintain the academic pace of his class with rather intense and conscientious effort. The school, however, became concerned that he would find the more competitive and advanced work of the top forms too great a strain, which could end in defeat. Although loyally devoted to this school, of his own volition he made the choice to move to a less demanding environment. Had he been rigidly held to his chronological age standards he would probably, at several points in his development, have required psychiatric help.

Norman was a small boy for his age and very conscious of it. He felt inadequate to the sports competition of his contemporaries. He avoided it at every opportunity, usually substituting the childish play of much younger companions or the spoiling indulgence of his sisters—seven and nine years older than himself. His parents had been divorced when he was still a baby, and his father had taken little interest in him beyond occasional visits of duty. The divorce had finally taken place because of the father's persistent homosexuality, although there is no evidence that the son knew of this—a problem Norman would some day have to face. Later the immature mother had, after several years, remarried an older man who had little interest in or understanding of children. Norman's own father's neglect of him and his mother's anxious protection of him (expressing her own emotional needs after the divorce) led her to center inordinate attention and considerable pampering on the little fellow. Her overprotection, combined with his own sense of size inferiority, led him to subconscious refusal to "grow up."

Intellectually able, full of fun and humor, he sought attention by "playing the clown." His success was immense—he was endlessly skillful, and his humor had no outward bitterness nor harm in it. He made every imaginable attempt to avoid sports, and to escape from classroom and learning responsibilities or group activities which called for any personal responsibility. Gradually, he became quite as ready to use his antics in serious as well as in diverting situations and considerable evidence of repressed aggression appeared.

At first, everyone—old and young—naturally warmed to his nonsense, yet as it came to be recognized that he could be seriously handicapped by his refusal to grow up, much attention was given to helping him, with only sporadic good results. Finally psychiatric consultation was urged upon the mother. Having had some earlier unsatisfactory experience with it, which had evidently only increased Norman's self-consciousness and her confusion, she refused.

Finally, as the measures yet used were having far too little effect on the problem, she agreed to full psychological testing, which led on to able psychiatric consultation. Norman transferred to a school where tutorial instruction is individual, psychotherapy available, and sports de-emphasized. In this new setting he appears to be making good progress toward emotional maturing.

Able? Yes, but . . .

More distressing is the boy of outstanding ability, who lacks motivation and whose performance is mediocre or worse.

Lanny was the obviously brilliant son of a brilliant family. Entering boarding school at the age of eleven, it was hoped that he would there find sufficient stimulus and challenge to keep him alert and responsive. Though nearly two years younger than his classmates, he had a group test I.Q. of 169 as he entered seventh grade. He carried successfully, though not brilliantly, the full program plus an extra course and all the extracurricular activities in which his interest could be stimulated. His social behavior was quiet but within normal limits, and he found adequate physical expression in soccer, skiing, and woodcraft.

The following fall his I.Q. report was of a "probably apochryphal" I.Q. of 223, based on extrapolated values. This year, on parental request, no effort was made toward advanced courses, but he was drawn much further into extracurricular interests, the band, the glee club, piano study, shop work, printing, and sports. His studies seemed of little importance to him—he was frankly bored— unwilling to give reasonable time to their preparation if he could possibly escape to his reading, which was adult and voluminous. The decision was taken not to press him academically, but to foster and encourage all social growth. No one was surprised that he achieved credit in two courses and failed dismally the two whose patient exactitude he counted drudgery. Then came the time of decision. Obviously he couldn't repeat— nor should he continue to be in social competition two years ahead of him.

The parents were wondering about psychotherapy. The school vigorously opposed, and suggested a year off from study for broadening experience. Fate intervened with an opportunity for an around-the-world cruise on a sailing ship —under expert leadership and with good companionship. The experiment proved a total success. He returned for his final year relaxed, stimulated, much matured. His achievement included an extra course, honor grades, success in sports, music, crafts, school paper, dramatics, high citizenship standing and the winning of the award for loyalty and character. His case amply bore out the contentions of Dr. Johnson O'Connor that the many-aptitude boy will be restless and do badly unless nearly all of his aptitudes are challenged and used, but will achieve signal success if they are. His next secondary school failed to recognize and follow this principle, so another slump preceded his later fine success. No psychotherapy was needed, but without challenge stimulus and fun, extreme introversion might have necessitated it.

Fred was an enigma to his parents and to his day school headmaster. Despite an I.Q. of 123 or better, he had failed his final year in a good independent day school. He just didn't seem to want to work. He was most personable, alert, showed keen intelligence on occasion, but could seem to sustain no effort for a prolonged period. Earlier there had been some behavior difficulties in the school and disappointment in the home that he had had difficulty with studies, but this period seemed past. The great concern of all was for his bland acceptance of academic failure which his good ability might clearly have avoided. His father was a successful lawyer, of quiet temperament, somewhat retiring and unaware of Fred's need for companionable support. His mother was highly attractive, vital, eager to help her son and the two younger children despite many social and community demands upon her.

It was felt that Fred needed a fresh start, away from earlier conflicts and failures and the need for attracting attention. His assistant headmaster wrote of him:

> Fred has a great potential, and in a good boarding school with close supervision he should realize his potential. One teacher who might show a particular interest in him could get him headed right so that Fred could get his feet under him academically, taste success, and carry on normally without the need of exhibiting himself as a mischief-maker. Pride in a good showing, of which he is capable, should furnish the incentive for consistently good work and citizenship.

His mother answered a questionnaire as follows:

> We feel strongly that Fred must not form the impression that he has been "banished" from home for failure, or that he is missing a vital part of the home life that his brother and sister are still getting. We've tried to plant the idea that going away to school is a privilege of his age group and will try to keep him regularly informed of home activities so he will not feel he's missing anything.

> *How does he adjust to other boys of his own age?*
> Gregarious mixer, inclined to want to be the "boss" until shown otherwise, but is friendly and fun-loving, values his friendships, but candidly. I feel he lacks true

consideration, kindness and thoughtfulness. He still must learn to develop these qualities in relationships with others.

[She reports an underlying unrecognized jealousy of brother two years younger.]

What are his particular aversions and dislikes, if any?

It sounds facetious, but actually his two most evident aversions are (1) to responsibility and (2) to fish.

To what extent is your boy acquainted with the facts of reproduction?

Has had a thorough discussion of the subject with his father. [NOTE: It is "*a* discussion"—no follow-up.]

What particular development would you like to have school accomplish for your boy?

We want Fred to acquire an honest interest in the work he is doing, not simply to slide by with as little effort as possible. We would like to see him develop a sense of responsibility, to profitably channel his terrific drive, to form and then head toward a goal, and, generally, to find himself and settle down at peace with his world, eschewing his present insecurity and flightiness. That's a large slice of maturity for which to hope, but we trust that at your school he may find it.

Little was heard from or about the father. His visits to the school were brief—somewhat withdrawn—his comments about his son cryptic, often critical. The impression grew that an overaggressive, managing mother had discouraged the males of the family, yet her interest was tenacious, her discussions increasingly proved her intelligent, and open-minded, and her desire to help her son very eager and modest.

Fred started his boarding school life after repeated assurances that it was his desire. He was eager, it appeared, for a fresh start and realization of the potential all had told him he possessed. Special faculty guidance was assigned him—twice he wore out patient helpers with unresponsiveness—yet, at one time, he did astonishingly well in the course of a teacher he enjoyed—only to have this flare die down after a month or so. He drew away from the approaches of his contem-

poraries—sought and played with younger boys and too
frequently teased or bullied them. Achievement, even though
he was repeating some material of his previous year's work,
was disappointingly low. He complained of the difficulty of
the work, and the lack of time to accomplish what many less
able and well-prepared classmates managed with success and
satisfaction.

Guidance efforts met blandly regretful responses and
clearly protective empty promises to try. Finally school and
parents turned to psychological testing for more revelation.
In the Wechsler-Bellevue test an I.Q. of 125 or better was
confirmed. Significant excerpts from the psychologist's report of the full emotional battery follow:

> If one judged him from the standpoint of his Rorschach
> productivity (10 responses), it would be necessary to state
> that he is virtually inert and uncooperative. This would
> be an error, since he is able to offer good evidence of
> inner living of a self-directive and empathetic nature and
> is capable of good organization. But there is no doubt
> that he is a very repressed youngster who is satisfied to
> meet the minimum requirements of a situation and who
> tends to retreat into inaction when he feels he is faced
> with possible failure . . . In other words, he clings too
> closely to safe and conventional ideas because any other
> approach introduces the threat of being wrong. This
> threat is associated with a very high level of aspiration
> which, by its very altitude, intensifies fear of failure
> regardless of his intellectual level. Boys of this type are
> sometimes inhibited in new situations which are not
> clearly structured for them, and are likely to take some
> time before they fulfill expectations . . .

> In summary, the test battery reveals an adolescent boy
> of superior intelligence who is experiencing difficulty at
> this time with concentration and attention because of his
> fear of falling short of paternal demands and expecta-
> tions. He is basically sound in his personality organiza-
> tion in spite of repression of affectional needs and hostile-
> provocative fantasies and external manifestations. If his
> father could be more lovingly paternal and less judg-
> mental in his relation with this youngster, one could

expect him to give a better account of himself, since he may sense the father's insufficient faith in him. This factor also suggests that those who work with him might attempt a sympathetic but firm approach.

The father was astonished—both at Fred's image of him and his need of him—said he'd try to fulfill it. Some months seem to have wrought relatively little change in either boy or father and it appears that a psychotherapist must take the place of the father who does not fully understand and feel his son's need.

Real Fathers—and Substitutes

It is interesting to see that an overwhelming proportion of boys who are ineffective in measuring up to their potential are those who lack adequate father contact and identification. By contrast, those who are overconcerned and over-ambitious in relation to their capacity have often almost too close an identification and serious concern for living up to paternal or maternal expectations. Adolescents who fall into this latter classification are usually easy to locate. Those lacking stable identifications may prove more puzzling. In the case of both, a sincere effort should be made to deal with their problems on the level of the school, rather than to seek first the help of psychiatry. There are times, however, when extreme lack of father identification, or fear of paternal rejection, can only be handled with outside psychiatric help. Often this can best be directed at the parent, rather than the boy. His gain can come through the parent. Oftentimes the psychiatrist's share in such a situation need be only brief. Once it is fully understood by those involved, including the mother, the school can usually carry on effectively without further professional assistance.

There are, of course, extreme cases in which a parent cannot or will not change his attitude. Then a "father substitute" may be necessary. Occasionally, a boarding school may be fortunate enough to work out such an arrangement, either as a result of the student's seeking, or of the teacher's, which will be emotionally satisfactory for the boy. A school with a carefully planned program of mature, trained advisorship will certainly try to fill his need. It is, however, important to remember my earlier cautions on this point. Such requests, or demands, upon a teacher, young or old, can be excessive, both in the time and the emotional energy required. Likewise, the teacher, in justice to himself as well as to his job with others, must guard against overinvolvement.

Timid and Anxious

The hypersensitive boy is not unusual in the adolescent years, when fears are certainly more common than we adults easily recall. Many still retain a fear of the dark. Fear of bodily injuries will lead some to withdraw from the sports competition and the adventure for which they secretly long, with consequent risk of introversion. Most young people will do their best to conceal these fears, but the emotional energy consumed by them may be so great as to be very disturbing. It is well for the schoolmaster to be fully informed in advance of known trauma and to be constantly on the alert for the customary secrecy with which the adolescent is concealing any anxiety. Any extreme demonstration of fear should be the source of immediate investigation.

We have already discussed anxiety over school work or other social and environmental demands. More commonly concealed, are worries over which the youth has no control, such as the size of his nose or ears, characteristics in the family which give him fear for his own future, or occasionally social ridicule. Often overconcern for family finances, the progress and happiness of siblings, and illness in the family may be other pressing concerns. If at all possible, it is valuable to learn these worries in a natural and informal way. Frequently, however, they are deeply hidden and the overconcerned child will make the greatest show of unconcern. A fairly reliable indicator of anxiety, as mentioned before, is the scores achieved on the digit span and digit symbol test of the Wechsler. Once anxiety is clearly demonstrated, it may well take full psychological testing to bring out its sources, and psychiatric help to alleviate its effects.

Dishonest

Among the invaluable lessons which psychology has brought to teachers is the recognition that dishonesty is almost always the outcome of insecurity and fear. The youth who lies usually does it for fear of punishment. He who cheats in lessons does it for fear of failure, or of the discovery of ignorance which he has been assiduously hiding. The tall-storyteller may perform in order to gain status, or even sympathy.

Often less easy to understand are those who steal. The theft may fill a need, providing some object which will provide status, or equipment for a desired activity. Again, it may be a form of boasting, shared with one or two contemporaries, and subconsciously motivated by the desire to be daringly "bad" when the boy has failed to achieve status on a more positive basis. Usually, dishonesty in the adolescent period can be dealt with by the understanding schoolmaster, with the help of a boy's contemporaries. Realistic discipline may be needed, particularly if the explanation is a relatively clear-cut one.

More complicated are those dishonesties which appear compulsive, and for which the adolescent may have no adequate conscious explanation. These certainly fall into the province of the psychiatrist and should have his prompt help. These cases may be complex, and the original diagnosis very difficult to achieve. Once found by the psychiatrist, cure may be relatively simple. Here again, may I caution about the effects of inadequate father identification for the youth. If he does not feel he can maintain character, reputation, and achievement which are comparable to his dad's, or can secure his father's approval and desire for his own company, he may well, often in most devious ways, end up by responding to outside stimuli toward dishonesty and related anti-social behavior. The inner needs which compel him may be very hard to trace.

Chuck, aged twelve and a half, was the son of a successful doctor in a small New England town. The father was particularly busy, as he had added to the normal duties and strains of his profession a number of independent business enterprises. In the process of caring for his many affairs, Dad had developed the habit of most economical management of family matters and always sought to train Chuck in economy. Chuck himself was a pleasant, rather easy-going youngster, somewhat ineffective and not very attractive. He had had difficulty in learning reading; however, he made a generally fair adjustment to his contemporaries, applied himself to his studies, and gradually acquired a more outgoing attitude. Increasingly, he delighted family and contemporaries by academic and social progress. Formerly gangling and clumsy, he became able to achieve some success in sports.

Suddenly, and without any warning, numerous articles began to disappear in Chuck's dormitory—items of clothing, a baseball glove, several baseballs, other sports equipment, and, finally, money. No one in the group dreamed that cheerful, happy, inoffensive Chuck could be the culprit. His admission, although slow in coming, was very complete. His explanation was simple. Other boys had more luxurious belongings than he. He had asked his parents for certain items which they had told him were extravagant. To gain status, not only among his schoolmates, from whom he had taken them, but in the eyes of friends at home, he had helped himself. With the understanding of the parents, and several patient and careful discussions with Chuck, the whole matter was straightened out without complication. He accepted normal punishments, and soon re-established himself in the regard and affection of his friends.

Andy was a highly personable youngster, handsome and athletic. His parents were very social and successful. Early in Andy's school career he had considerable learning difficulties, particularly with reading and spelling. He was sent to boarding school at the age of eleven to receive help for this difficulty. In the succeeding years Andy made good progress in overcoming his reading difficulties, although the early steps were steep and painful. Insecurity did turn up from time to time in the academic work—a tendency to cheat or evade responsibility, but little by little this was overcome. Andy became known as a good and faithful worker, although no great scholar.

Still, it was notable that Andy always sought out as companions some of the less secure of his contemporaries and that often they got into mischief—not always of an aboveboard sort. There was a good bit of teasing and sometimes bullying, and a considerable amount of evasion of school rules and responsibilities. All this was combined with the attitude that the value of truth was wholly dependent upon whether it paid off or not. There were also incidents of articles taken, though usually these were accompanied by plausible excuses that they had been "lost and found." Then, for a considerable period of time, Andy appeared to be outgrowing his insecurity and enjoying real success. He was doing well academically, and had won the respect of his contemporaries.

Suddenly, without warning, numbers of articles began to disappear from his dormitory and from his friends' belongings. After initial reluctance he admitted the thefts. He was at a loss to give any reasonable explanation. He felt he had worked sincerely to overcome his weaknesses and gain strength. He "simply felt" a wave of desire to go back to his old bad habits. Nor could the parents give an explanation for the difficulty. The school recommended psychiatric consultation and advice. The psychiatrist discovered Andy was one of those boys—rather too common these days—whose insecurity stemmed from the lack of a stable relationship with a father figure. As an infant, his father was "off in the war," although his mother sought in every way to provide warmth and full home life. The father's absence was very upsetting to the mother, who for a considerable time tried to overcome her own insecurity by activities which took some of her attention from the little boy. On his return, the father felt very distant from his son, unable to establish understanding and rapport, and was frequently frustrated by the boy's difficulties and problems. This case was relatively easily straightened out by explaining to the parents the boy's sense of rejection, and his other fears. He went from boarding school back to his home and public school. In the latter, demands upon his intellect were not too great, and his father became his incessant companion and friend. Andy is today a thoroughly happy, well-adjusted and, within his limitations, successful boy.

Quiet and Very Tractable

Perhaps the most overlooked and yet the most susceptible to emotional illness is the extremely withdrawn boy. This youngster will usually be prone to fantasy, possibly threatening approaching schizophrenia. It is likely that he will be the quiet type, and frequently an outer conformist to school customs, routine, and demands. He will evade the boisterousness and aggression of sports if he can, will retire to a corner with a book in which he will lose himself, and will be oblivious to or rebuff the efforts of his classmates who seek to draw him into their activities and fun. He is likely to resist adult efforts to "draw him out," or to talk about his family and home life. He is certain to avoid all competitive situations. His assignments will come in late, or not at all; and in due course it will be quite apparent that his presence is in the flesh, not the spirit. Naturally, adults will interest themselves in trying to "bring this boy out," to strike a spark of enthusiasm for a hobby, even seek to elicit the source of his self-concern and reality evasion. Occasionally, the constant and persistent efforts of a mature contemporary or slightly older boy will draw out such a youngster, as in the case of Mandy (below). In other cases (see Ranny, below), psychotherapy is indicated.

Mandy entered his second boarding school at the age of eleven. His mother had divorced his father—apparently not a very strong or admirable character—and in his early years the bond between mother and son had been very close. His mother came from a socially prominent family in a Midwestern city. She was talented, artistic, literary. A sensitive person, she was distressed over the break-up of her own marriage; at first she inclined to neglect old friends and to center her life and interest on her two sons. The older brother was rugged, outgoing, reasonably aggressive, and made the adjustment to the loss of his father with relatively little difficulty. Gradually, the mother came to realize that she was overprotecting young Mandy; that she too needed to live a life more her own, and that in their closeness lay danger. So, at ten, on the advice of family friends, Mandy was sent to his first boarding school. When this was found to lack both stimulation and warmth, he was moved to another.

Mandy's I.Q. was 151; he was advanced in reading, somewhat limited in social experience with other children, small in stature and physically timid in sport or competition. No one could have had a sweeter nature or more delightful manner. Meeting the rough and tumble of boarding school and of contemporary competition, Mandy quickly labeled it as an alien element. He displayed no outward, active homesickness, but frequently stated that he just didn't like and couldn't participate in sports; that he thought his classmates were rather crude people, whom his mother certainly wouldn't enjoy. He would, at every opportunity, go to his room to delve deep in a book, mature beyond his years, and read with great joy and appreciation volumes of culturally valuable material. He shared contemporary activity as required, no more.

Soon many boys developed concern for Mandy and sought the help of adults. Their gestures of friendliness, invitations to participate in games, their personal interest—all had been quietly, politely and thoroughly rebuffed.

At this point, a faculty wife of sympathetic temperament volunteered for the role of mother substitute, which she performed admirably, entertaining him in her apartment, talking long hours with him about his reading; relating it at every point to the life about him. Gradually she was able to draw into these discussions other sensitive, intellectually active boys, whose interests coincided with Mandy's. Little by little he came to welcome a few of them as companions and friends, although only a few weeks previous he had labeled them barbarians.

In particular, he found amusement and interest in one companion, who was, in truth, a barbarian, though an intellectual one. They became fast friends and shared many mature interests, while John helped Mandy to catch up on childhood joys and outdoor exercise. Later Mandy became a very respectable soccer player, a good and enthusiastic skier, and both boys read, studied, and participated in the school's intellectual life, from poetry and debating to the student council, with real vigor and determination. Both were on the honor roll. Their friendship and mutual support was most wholesome. In three succeeding years Mandy became as vigorous, normal, and energetic a person as one of his small stature, and sensitive nature might. The friendship of the two reached out to include many others, and Mandy became not only a social individual but an outstanding leader of his class and head of the student government. This latter post he handled with rare devotion and fortunately without a sense of superiority. Learning to tolerate the frailties and weaknesses of others, and to help them, gradually became a source of increasing strength and confidence to him.

In his succeeding school he and his friend John both lived up to their earlier promise, finished their college preparation a year ahead of schedule, so that each had the opportunity of a year of stimulating study and adventure abroad before entering college. In this period Mandy reported that our understanding and sympathetic handling had, he felt, saved him from "going off the deep end." He felt happy, secure and successful.

Ranny was the eldest of six children, who had been brought up in a warm and intimate family life—what most observers would call an ideal home. When we first made contact with this family, it was reported that Ranny liked the sister nearest his own age, had some friction with the next oldest sister and brother, but was devoted to his two little brothers. He was described by his family as being timid, sensitive, quiet, imaginative, careless, easily fatigued, easily discouraged, fond of humor, truthful, appreciative of literature and animals.

His early schooling was in the local country school. Being a boy of very high ability, with a Wechsler-Bellevue verbal score of 132, which indicated startlingly high scores in comprehension, arithmetic, and similarities, he clearly outshone his classmates and found very little in the classroom subject material to challenge him, nor did Ranny seek to reach out for such challenge, except as he became a voracious reader, eager for facts and history, and contemptuous of fiction. His parents reported rather inadequate adjustment to his contemporaries and commented that he acted in a younger fashion than the boys in his class. Also that in play he liked those things which he could do alone. Family and teacher were distressed that this obviously very able boy was not sufficiently challenged in making outgoing adjustment in school and also doing mediocre work totally inconsistent with his ability. The family's efforts to seek for the keynote produced very little. Finally he was sent to a small tutoring school a thousand miles away, run by a family friend, where some headway was made through devoted individual attention, academically and socially, and constant reassurance and guidance, and especially pressure.

The following fall he entered boarding school, having completed the necessary material for entering his seventh grade class where he was placed in an able, fast group. His test record displayed high reading skills, excellent mathematical reasoning, but composition skills equivalent to that of a third-grader. As he started his year he seemed moderately interested in his school subjects and activities but inclined toward an individualistic point of view, challenged only by informational subjects and mathematics. The study of basic skills in English and language bored him and he took increasing pride in doing as little as possible on daily assignments, hoping to satisfy his teacher and classmates with high test grades. He participated in shop, art, printing, dramatics and sports, but with very little cooperation or enthusiasm. Particularly he sought to withdraw or escape from sports. Though physically slight, he could participate in the games and was encouraged to do so, but responded only under compulsion.

At times, when he might determine his own activities or pursue his own interests, he was often friendly, jolly, and humorous. Increasingly, however, the withdrawing tendency continued. Assignments were neglected and nothing but frequent and firm, though very friendly, pressure kept him up with his academic work. He had to give up free time, even part of his holiday, for making up in his studies. Efforts to stimulate him by giving him responsibility of individual study assignments which would bring him distinction in the class bore little fruit.

Gradually the picture developed into that of a sit-down strike, in which Ranny was determined to outwit and win over both his parents and his teachers. At no time was there any direct objection to learn or to be anywhere but in this particular school.

Gradually the impression grew among his teachers that he was utilizing the situation with considerable delight as a means of getting attention both from them and from his parents. It was hoped that after the first summer holiday new maturity might produce more confidence, and acceptance and assumption of responsibilities. During the opening weeks of the following fall term there was a flurry of hope, but soon the old pattern reappeared and "sit-down strikes" increased to the point where the anxiety of both parents and school was very grave indeed.

At this point he was observed by a friendly psychiatrist visiting the school, who promptly picked him out as an object of concern and said, "There is a really sick boy. He should have immediate psychiatric help." A complete psychological testing was promptly accomplished, with the parents' cooperation. Scores on the digit span and digit symbol tests were in alarming contrast to the other high scores and the emotional test battery brought out deep disturbances. The psychologist summarized the case as follows:

The test findings delineate a young adolescent of very superior intelligence who lives on an abstract plane and has a high level of aspiration which his psychosexual difficulties prevent him from fulfilling. His intelligence conceals the fact that his level of maturation is quite low, so that avoidance of social interaction is utilized as a means of defense against self-exposure. He is deficient in empathy, indulges in a great deal of regressed fantasying, involving hedonistic and aggresive actions, and can be expected to be erratic in his achivements. Underlying pleasure drives are associated with a wish for leisure in which to pursue his unrealistic daydreams, so that his passive resistiveness serves the purpose of giving him this leisure and allowing him to express an indirect antisocial attitude. The diagnostic impression is consistent with schizoid psychopathy which is not likely to respond to motivational efforts by school personnel. Psychiatric treatment rather than guidance is indicated.

Psychiatric treatment was promptly instituted with the full cooperation of the parents and the boy was withdrawn from the school to relieve environmental pressures and to give him enough freedom in the local school and home environment while treatment continued. After nearly six months of psychotherapy his personality structure is still not strong enough to meet a social situation, but it is felt that the psychotherapy will be successful. This clearly was a case where psychiatric help would certainly have been very advantageous earlier. The diagnosis brought out by the psychological test battery, had it been available earlier, could possibly have prevented the severeness of the ensuing difficulties.

Parents Divorced

The boy who comes from the "broken home" may or may not need help. The very fact of this dislocation in life calls for an awareness of possible trauma and special needs. Presumably the school's preliminary interviews with parent and student have helped to establish the degree to which divorce has upset self-acceptance, general emotional maturing, or has developed marked insecurity. Commonly, this youngster can be made secure in a normally warm environment, and through encouraging other interpersonal relationships. If security does not increase, professional help is indicated. In our experience it is usually possible to enlist constructive cooperation of both parents, even though their own relationship to each other may not be free of conflict.

The four Hawthorne boys lived a most happy, securely companionable life with their parents. A more ideal home would have been difficult to imagine, until gradually changing interests and a "third person" led the adults to the mutually accepted decision of divorce, soon after which each remarried. Each exercised great care to conduct his or her own relations maturely. Both were painstaking in avoiding strain for the children. The result was continuing friendship and cooperation between the parents—two happy homes and four happy and welcoming parents for the boys. They felt fortunate and rich beyond most, as indeed they were.

I could recount innumerable instances where divorce has helped, rather than handicapped the children. For the young people, the outcome depends on the maturity and cooperativeness of the parents, their concern for the children, and the conditions which led to the separation. These conditions, of course, may have produced excessive strain. However, it is well to remember that the symptoms of disturbance may be much the same as those from a so-called "normal" home. The very fact of the divorce clearly ends much previous pressure, although its accumulated psychological trauma may call for later professional help. Only in those cases where an immature parent, or both parents, continue to seek to hurt the other through the children, or are themselves deeply disturbed, need the settled divorce situation produce new damage.

They Don't Care

Rejection of a child may be closely interwoven in a divorce situation, but can quite as often exist without divorce.

Another boy who may need considerable attention is the youngster whose parents are extremely busy or are away from home a great deal, or who fail to keep in touch with him by telephone and letter. Frequently this youngster is actually rejected; certainly he will feel that he is, and not infrequently he will develop a very aggressive response. Commonly these parents, particularly the father, will be quite unaware of the effect of their attitudes and neglect upon their son. Often this results from similar treatment received from their own parents, or very rigid and structured attitudes seen in the grandparental generation. Such background may engender a lack of appreciation for the normal parental function, and an inability to communicate the warmth and rapport needed by any child.

Customarily, these situations have their roots in a time far earlier than the adolescent period. The rejection, actual or implied, is usually well established and felt before adolescence; yet adolescence is the period when such rejection is especially dramatic and explosive. Much of the literature about juvenile delinquents points to neglect as its foundation. In my opinion, this child should not go to the normal boarding school. He should have a foster or substitute home of a warm and suitable emotional climate as early as the problem is discernible.

George was one of two sons born during the war. His mother, herself brought up under the most strait-laced discipline, had finally escaped her rigidly confining home and parents by employing her talents in a career. Nonetheless, her own mother retained great power over her. She fell in love with a man in military service, only to find the marriage vehemently opposed by her mother, whom she defied, and went through with the marriage. The father was on foreign soil when George was born and the grandmother did everything to make the youngster unwelcome and *de trop* in the house, even trying to turn her daughter against her own son and her husband. For a time the mother, clinging to both, reduced the amount of her professional activity. The father returned on leave. Considerable difficulty ensued within the grandparental home. Later he was again called back to duty. This time another youngster was on the way. Continued struggles between mother and daughter followed, the mother constantly urging the daughter to part from the so-called "worthless" husband. Finally, a separation did come about and the young mother went on with her career, which prospered.

In the meantime both boys were very nearly completely neglected. They saw very little of their mother, living usually with a most unsympathetic grandmother or other relatives or friends, and occasionally accompanying the mother in her business travels. An emotionally immature person herself, she had no concept of motherhood, and was preoccupied with achieving name, fame and money, to compensate for the trials of her own childhood. George, the older of the two boys, clearly showed many evidences of insecurity and developed a very aggressive temperament. Limited in academic ability, he had not done well in school and clearly showed the lack of a stable and affectionate environment.

He was placed in boarding school at the age of eleven, largely on the advice of his mother's second husband, a fine and devoted person who had been quick to see the needs of the boys. His visits to the school and his attention during the vacations were understanding of the problem that the boys faced. The school gave George remarkable personal attention, one faculty member playing the part of substitute father and his wife of substitute mother. When these teachers were no longer available, another man took on the challenging task. George's behavior was variable, sometimes affectionate, constructive and responsive, and at other times highly rebellious and aggressive. As he matured physically, his relations to younger children and to his classmates displayed dangerous signs of frustration. It appeared that from time to time he felt the need to reject his susbtitute father figure for the sake of the emotional experience of "making up"—or establishing confidence of dominance.

When tested on the Wechsler-Bellevue scale there was one strange and startling test result, contrasting with an otherwise rather average performance. George failed both the profile and the hand assembly test. His younger brother, when tested, failed the profile assembly. The psychologists reports, "one can only conclude that this female profile must have deep significance for the brothers."

As of this writing, George's future and program are unsettled. A change of school has been made so that he will live in a less demanding environment, which will subject him to fewer tensions and where he will not be competing with other students of much greater ability. There is, however, no resolution of the continuing total rejection by the mother, despite all effort made thus far to help her understand George's and his brother's needs to place them ahead of professional ambitions. Purely as conjecture, this writer feels that unless and until this problem is faced squarely, George is headed for increasing maladjustment and trouble.

The entire question of rejection is very much a cultural one these days. Particularly among the competitive and materialistically successful segments of society, we find increase of professional and business demands upon father and social demands upon mother which unquestionably reduce the realistic capacity of even well-meaning parents to be "good" parents. This whole phenomenon has been discussed at such length in numerous articles and books that it needs no elaboration. The schoolmaster should be ever on guard for rejection that may be quite unconscious, and exist more in the mind of the child than in the parent's actual feeling. The understanding teacher can often help such a parent, or if need be, guide him to psychological help.

The Rebel—Don't Overlook Me

At this point my readers may be wondering where I have left the boy who frequently causes so much difficulty in adolescence—the restless boy, the boaster, the bully, the seeker for excessive attention. While he may, for a time, be one of the most difficult to assimilate into the group, he is certainly far more normal than the excessively withdrawn boy and far less likely to need the attention of a psychiatrist. Nearly all of the phenomena he will present are the results of insecurity. He confirms the adage that "the empty drum makes the loudest noise." He is so fearful that he cannot compete in legitimate channels that he tries to dominate the weaker boys. He may go so far as to try to reinforce his own sense of importance by leading a gang.

The attention-seeking boy, with his thousand and one defensive mechanisms, class disturbance, incessive talkativeness, incongruous oddities of behavior, or the leader of rebellion against adults, can be the bane of a teacher's existence. Yet, if his pride permitted it, he would break down and face up to the fact that he doesn't feel competent either to compete with his peers or to live up to the expectations of his parents and teachers. This lad needs encouragement, help and firmness, often combined with friendly ignoring of his antisocial behavior. Only in those cases where the symptoms are far more extreme and continuous than those commonly encountered or where he insistently aligns himself with others who show similar symptoms need he be of deep social concern or require psychiatric referral.

Outwardly Adjusted?—Beware!

Caution should be expressed that successful adaptation to contemporary environment, and absence of unusual outward behavior manifestation, do not necessarily indicate full mental health and strength. There probably are many apparently "well-adjusted" youngsters in our schools, whose need for help remains unrecognized. This is a big question for the schoolmaster. Personality Inventories, like those men-

tioned in the section on testing, or short and simple projective tests can be used individually, or in relatively small
groups to locate minor disturbances. Lay counseling will
probably prove adequate in the great majority of such cases.
Yet, what potential tragedies could be averted if those in real
need received early, expert help!

PSYCHIATRIC REFERRAL AND TREATMENT

Psychiatric referral by the school may or may not be
fraught with complications. Fortunately, the day has gone
by when most parents viewed psychiatric consultation as
threat of emotional illness or insanity. Even the past few
years have brought marked advance in parental acceptance
of the psychiatrist's helpfulness. Rarely, however, will parents be eager to have psychological testing carried out until
the schoolmaster has known their child for some time, and
can also, through the usual educational tests and measurements, demonstrate the need for further investigation to
identify the cause of learning or behavior difficulties. Frequently discussion of the results of a Wechsler-Bellevue test
will lead them to accept full psychological testing, often with
genuine gratitude.

When possible, we find it constructive for the psychologist
to give his tests in the familiar environment of the school,
where it may be known that others are taking similar tests,
rather than in the strange setting of the professional office.
We have found the commonly accepted battery of House-
Tree-Persons, and other figure-drawing tests, the Bender-
Gestalt, the Rorschach, and the Thematic Apperception
tests, which are now available on different age levels, together provide adequate diagnosis. If psychiatric help is
needed, careful interpretation of test results is usually convincing to all but the most skeptical parents. The interpretation can be made to parents by the testing psychologist, by

a psychiatrist, or, in certain instances, by the schoolmaster— preferably the headmaster. *This decision should be left to the parents.* Sometimes the experienced schoolmaster's interpretation, although probably not as expert as the professional one, can seem less alarming, and can bring the parent to acceptance of psychiatric consultation more readily than a report from the specialist.

Our experience underlines the conclusion that the most obvious disturbances often prove, on testing, to be not as important from the mental health point of view as some of the less easily observable ones. Many a withdrawn and wholly conforming student has a far more serious basic illness than the evident rebel or troublemaker. Parents of the first boy may be difficult to convince of their son's need for help. The latter individual is inevitably very susceptible to contemporary opinion and influence. The school with a good degree of student government, with a feeling for democracy and responsibility, can work rapid wonders with his behavior.

Recalling my earlier comparison of adolescence with necessary illness, we need to re-remind ourselves that all of us, laymen or professional, are therapists when dealing with this age group. The question at issue is the severity of the illness and the degree of skill needed to cure it. Although we should be alert to the fact that actual professional psychotherapy may be needed, it is, in my judgment, seldom necessary over a prolonged period of time. When used, let it be of relatively brief duration and distinctly of the psychotherapeutic type. Possibly intensive therapy may be needed at the outset, but thereafter more occasional visits and more casual guidance usually "fill the bill." Frequently parents of an apparently disturbed adolescent need therapy and guidance rather than the youth. The psychiatrist may be most successful in working with him through his family.

Many psychiatrists have found in actual practice that it

is quite possible for them to treat an adolescent indirectly through a teacher. This requires frequent consultation with the teacher. This is, of course, of infinite value to the teacher as part of his own professional training. This approach may also have the advantage of more continuing and constant contact than is possible for the psychiatrist and patient, and often causes far less self-concern.

I would enter an urgent plea against psychoanalysis for any but the most seriously ill adolescent. In the process of personality formation, and the growth of the self which he is undergoing, he cannot very well unravel and rewind threads which are as yet very tenuous for him, or those which were strongly overstructured by unusually dominant early home influence. Nor, if he tried to, would he come out the same wholesome, integrated individual that he might be if he "muddles" through normal life experience, working out his own conflicts to a satisfactory solution, with sympathetic but not overintensive guidance.

A criticism voiced by many schoolmasters entrusted with the daily care and follow-up of students under psychiatric treatment is that some psychiatrists fail to take the responsible teacher fully into their confidence regarding the nature of the difficulty, its severity, and the progress of treatment. Psychiatrists vary widely in this respect, some adopting a very understanding and cooperative attitude. If the psychiatrist is content to leave the child in a given school, it would appear that he must confide in his lay co-worker, and share his conclusions, providing the school with specific and continuing guidance as to its part in the plan. Similarly the teacher and headmaster should fully share with the doctor whatever knowledge they may have and report to him frequently. It is good for the patient to know that schoolmaster and physician are cooperating closely on his behalf.

Occasionally, a youngster may be the victim of a situation neurosis, with the school the apparently disturbing influence. If such a situation cannot be readily adjusted, quick removal of the individual from the environment is the only answer. Commonly, I believe, such situations spring from early interpersonal family problems, which the child has transferred to the school. Surely in any of these, the school should feel no criticism in the child's removal. The school will probably experience relief, but in any event the sincerely devoted school teacher's ego need not suffer!

In some of these cases, as in certain others of severe disturbance, the school will face a dilemma. The rebellious adolescent may well behave so outrageously as to invite immediate dismissal, either for his own good, that of the group, or both. Where possible, the probable trauma from this step should be avoided, and parents asked to withdraw the boy quietly. If, however, despite patient and skillful handling by the school, group morale or health are severely threatened, the interests of the many must come before those of the individual. The inevitability of this lesson may then be what the psychiatrist needs to win his patient's trust.

Particularly important, it seems to me, is the comment made elsewhere in this volume that a psychiatrist should not ask exceptional treatment of a patient in terms of curriculum or school activities. Surely it will not help the patient's adjustment to the environment if he feels that he is being considered substantially "different" or is having unusual concessions made to him. When special allowances must be made, they should appear to be the result of a decision by the school rather than a request from the therapist or parents. Psychiatrists dealing with independent school children should, however, be well aware that most of our schools are capable of considerable flexibility and glad to exercise it constructively. Especially important, I feel, are the proper adjustment of the study-load to the individual's capacity, and the opportunity for creative and emotional outlets. Sometimes the school may not have judged these needs accurately, nor have known of interests and relaxations that might help a particular boy—for example, music, dramatics, art, crafts, woodlore, nature study, or the pursuit of any hobby of absorbing interest.

"And Gladly Teach"

A vital need of the adolescent is the time and opportunity to escape. Most schools are very busy, highly organized places where the undoubted values of group life can easily be over-emphasized. There should always be the opportunity, both in the scheduled day and at times of special need, for the youth to get off by himself and "set and think" no matter how idle his daydreaming may seem. Fortunate is the school located in a natural country setting where God and beauty can appear near and ready to encourage or heal (45).

We adults often underestimate the adolescent's natural susceptibility to, and desire for, religion. Cynical as he may seem about structured religion or an Almighty deity, this is one of the central concerns of his life. It probably has never been, and may never again be, as important to him.

Youth will be more critical and demanding of his own contemporaries than is the adult. Criticism and demanding standards are more easily accepted from one's peers than from the grownup who represents the outer personal authority which the adolescent is trying to discard. Carefully guided substitution of the morale and authority of the contemporary group is socially and emotionally maturing, presenting to the youth a situation which is immediate and real to him. Wise is the teacher or the headmaster who will not only allow but encourage students to handle their own affairs, with an absolute minimum show of adult authority on his own part. He must, of course, tacitly assume the existence of his authority and exercise it when necessary, with definiteness and firmness, and calmly if possible, yet when righteous indignation is called for, it should come as an act of faith by which it is well for the student to be guided!

This writer does not recommend a completely permissive and unstructured atmosphere; the adolescent is too uncertain of himself to accept such a situation without un-needed turmoil and pain. Nor will he respect the abdication of authority in any matters commonly accepted as vital in his culture or his home.

The adolescent does appreciate respect for the secrecy of his own inner life which he chooses not to share with adults, and often only very timidly with his peers. He will respond best to those who understand, and who trust his capacity to solve many of his own problems.

Particularly will he respond to the opportunity for assumption of responsibility and activities which bring him status. Made jobs rarely fool the adolescent. If the community can be so organized that he senses the need of his responsible participation, is given a concern for the happy adjustment of the general life, and sometimes for the guidance of others, we find that his maturity will often far exceed our and his parents' expectations. Yet he needs the faith that the friendly adult is always at hand to help him up when he stumbles, give him at pat on the back, and point him to a quick start on the continuing road.

The adolescent, highly sensitive, is capable of tremendous idealism, and yearns for association with such enterprises. If they can be made availabe to him, in close collaboration with his peers, if they have meaning and value to the ideal world that he seeks, then they will provide both present satisfaction and the patterning of good democratic citizenship. As he gets "his head out of his belly," the adolescent feels he must save the world. He should be given innumerable opportunities toward this goal. He—even more perhaps, she —will be something of an actor, switching quickly from one role to another. Since he does not yet know and fully accept himself, he is ready to identify with Jeanne d'Arc, Roald Amundsen, Abraham Lincoln, or the causes which they and others represented. He may also emulate the ideas and causes of parents and other admired grownups. The adolescent must be able to lose himself to find himself, be simultaneously anonymous and full of identity. He passes through frustrations, challenges, threats, panic—even imagined death —to achieve imagined or genuine heroism. The adolescent's capacity for maturity which is nearly adult has been demonstrated in every war, and in the meeting of nearly every great human or community crisis.

If we, in our culture, can learn to give youth more dignity, more credit, and more respect—if we admit him earlier to the society of mature and responsible people, we shall find him less inclined to restlessness and troublemaking, suffering fewer distressed growth experiences. Our culture is slowly moving forward to greater understanding of our young people. May we hasten this process.

I conclude with the appeal to my own profession to think as highly of our calling as it deserves, that we may be worthy of our opportunity:

> As childhood merges into adolescent youth the school also becomes a cultural workshop of unique power. In a democracy this power is far-reaching because the school, whether private or public, is charged with the double task of educating its youth both as individuals and as future citizens. The school system thereby becomes the chief instrument by which society perpetuates and renews itself. Teachers become agents in transmitting our cultural heritage and defining the duties of citizenship. The adolescent boys and girls whom they teach are beneficiaries and participants. It is a vast mutual enterprise in which both the individual and the nation have a stake [21, p. 449].

A developmental approach to the teaching task proves its merits. This approach does not rely upon rigid absolutes and remote goals, but fosters an awareness of the *ever-present maturity factors* which affect the behavior of the individual and the school group . . . Awareness of the maturity traits and trends . . . enable her to detect significant individual deviations. A developmentally minded teacher tends to gear her work to the developmental readiness of her pupils, and to adapt it to their creative energies. Above all, their curiosity and gifts for self-expression must be kept alive to safeguard the kind of mental growth which promotes mental health . . .

A vital teacher is one who has a knack for reaching individuals without singling them out . . . Such a teacher demonstrates one of the profound paradoxes of psychological growth. Growth of mind and personality takes a long time; but this growth also incorporates brief moments of significant experience.

A vital schoolroom multiples these moments. It has faith in the here and now. Citizenship remains the ultimate goal. But sufficient unto the day is the spirit of youth and "its immemorial ability to reaffirm the charm of existence" [21, p. 455].

10

SUMMARY

BENJAMIN H. BALSER, M.D.

There are a number of points which have been omitted and deserve introduction at this point to complete the text. Therefore, the next few paragraphs will contain new material and the summary will follow it.

One is frequently asked the age span of adolescence. The period of from thirteen to twenty is probably the average span of adolescence; yet youngsters are seen in preadolescence frequently, and young adults up to the age of twenty-five or more who still retain many adolescent characteristics and problems with which they need help. Girls approach adolescence on the average a year or so before boys, and both boys and girls of higher intelligence frequently enter adolescence at an earlier age. In working through the problems of adolescents, however, it does not necessarily follow that those with higher intelligence always enter adulthood at an earlier age. The factors of home, school, and social environments appear to be the major determinants of the rapidity with which the individual completes the major portion of his adolescence. Several case reports included in the preceding chapter are those of youngsters who were in preadolescence.

Though the focus of this book is on the different levels of therapy, several of the chapters discuss problems which are basic to all levels. The training of a psychiatrist dealing with adolescents is one such problem. He should have had some training in pediatric psychiatry as well as in adult psychiatry. Work with adolescents derives from an understanding of both these areas, and the actual experience in psychotherapy of adolescents raises new issues and questions which are not found in the training in either of the other levels. Few schools of medicine offer training in adolescent psychiatry per se. There are some didactic lectures and an occasional contact with an adolescent patient during the training periods of psychiatrists, but not much more than that. Another problem which is basic to all levels of therapy is that of the therapist's capacity to control his own anxiety as he is dealing with the adolescent. This is frequently provoked in problem situations that arise during the therapy. The therapist's understanding of his own drives and needs is important in helping him work out a satisfactory solution for problems presented by the patient.

The psychology of the adolescent is interesting in many respects, but most fascinating if viewed from the vantage point of the changing nature of the morals and customs among adolescents in different socioeconomic groups. What might be accepted as normal in one group may be foreign to another. For example, the use of "Sir" or a boy rising when a girl or adult enter the room are accepted without second thought in some socioeconomic levels. At other levels, this would be considered "sissy" or "put-on." On the other hand, some groups accept patched or torn clothing as rather standard equipment, whereas at other socioeconomic levels this could be embarrassing for the youngsters. There are some phenomena that are applicable to all groups, such as, interest in classical music. Adolescents at all levels will frequently consider this "long-haired stuff" and look down their noses at it.

The language of the adolescent contains many expressions which reflect the particular decade in which he is living, and it is important for the therapist to understand these expressions or be familiar with them. This enhances the therapeutic relationship and makes the therapist's interpretations more readily acceptable to the patient. At this particular time such expressions as "hacking around" (fooling around), being "sharp" or "cool" (being smart, aware, understanding) are fairly common expressions heard during the interview. In the male of the age of fourteen, one normally sees a sudden excessive interest in personal appearance. An extreme interest in dress, neatness, and cleanliness occurs as a transient phenomenon in many boys, yet, if taken as an isolated picture, is highly suggestive of the psychopathology of an obsessive-compulsive neurotic.

Group therapy has been advocated and practiced with adolescents. Personally, I have had no experience with such practice. It may be effective. Even with it, however, one feels that it is important for the adolescent to receive individual therapy if one wants to give the patient adequate help in establishing a sound homeostasis. Working with large groups of students in mental health seminars in private and public schools, one finds an enthusiastic reception plus a feeling that one effectively helps clarify the nature of mental health and mental illness, its recognition, and the approach to the correction of faults that may lie in those areas. It should be noted, however, that these groups consist mainly of normal adolescents, with only a sprinkling of youngsters with emotional problems.

The question of vocational counseling of adolescents has also been raised. If one considers this in terms of future channels of work or life endeavor, it would seem to me advisable to postpone such decision as a concrete plan until the later stages of adolescence or early adulthood. Recommendations for specific kinds of work to adolescents should be based upon the individual's intelligence and interests. Obviously, it is essential to have some concept of the individual's greatest potential in terms of augmenting it through college education if this is part of his goal. However, I am one who believes that a liberal arts education for the first two years will help any adolescent become a better human being and better adjusted to society and his fellow man. Most adolescents will not go on to college. Vocational counseling for these individuals would best be instituted from the sixteenth year onward.

Dr. Irene Josselyn, in her chapter on private practice, has made a number of important points, some of which deserve reiteration at this time. It is important with adolescents to develop a transference relationship as rapidly as possible. This at times may require an empathic attitude in early stages which may later be modified. Secondly, it is important to get the total family picture if one is dealing with an adolescent, and this usually means seeing the parents if it is at all possible. At times the therapist can treat both the adolescent and one parent. This will depend both on the problem presented and the judgment of the therapist. Treatment of both parents is rarely sucessful, in my experience. If it appears that both parents need help, it is far better to have them treated by different therapists. Occasionally, one finds it advisable to treat a parent or parents without directing treatment at the adolescent.

It is wise to set goals of therapy early. These can be modified if the situation requires it as therapy is continuing. Another point that Dr. Josselyn makes is the effectiveness of short-term treatment. This has been observed by most of the psychiatrists working with adolescents. The criticism has been raised that short-term therapy in adolescents may cover over the actual problems and that in later life they will recur. This is probably true in occasional instances, but one cannot subscribe to this as being a frequent occurrence. The basis for this statement has to do with personal experience with a group of forty short-term patients who were followed up fifteen to seventeen years after the original treatment period. Most of these youngsters have made an excellent adjustment following treatment and retained it up to the time of this follow-up study. It should be remembered that in private practice one sees the entire spectrum of emotional problems in adolescents ranging from mild disturbances to severe psychotic states. However, by far the majority (80 per cent plus) are youngsters who show mild to moderate disturbances. Moreover, many of these disturbances, if they appeared in the adult, would have to be regarded as signs of severe psychopathology. In the adolescent, they must be viewed as a developmental phenomenon.

At the level of private practice and school practice, some interesting situations arise. Because of the psychiatrist's direct association with the school, be it private or public school, students will come for appointments not only because they are referred by the masters, teachers, or the principals of the school, but also on their own. The incidence of self-referral is about 10 per cent, in my experience, varying at different schools with the climate of acceptance of psychiatry. These youngsters constitute a particularly interesting group for they are not only well motivated but are usually intelligent, have some knowledge of psychology (human), and respond rapidly to short-term therapy. It should not be taken for granted, however, that all such self-referred youngsters fall into this category. A fair number of them have problems which require more intensive treatment of longer duration. Perhaps one of the most important aspects of the presence of the psychiatrist on the school staff is the fact that he will reach the student earlier than would otherwise happen because of his availability and a growing awareness of his function. In schools that do not have psychiatrists on their staff, such consultation can readily be obtained at an early stage in the student's school life and need not wait until long observation or psychological tests have been instituted.

Psychiatric examination is no more traumatic than any other medical examination.

One should note that in a school practice the psychiatrist is at first looked upon askance. He may be referred to as the "head shrinker," or the "nut cracker," and by other epithets. It takes a relatively short period of time for the students to recognize the fact that he has no horns on his head, is as human as the next fellow, can understand a joke and the language of the adolescent, and is there to help. More recently students themselves have become conscious of the importance of emotional problems. They are becoming aware not only of the role that emotions play in their lives but also that something can be done about their unhappy feelings. As a result, one sees many of them becoming more tolerant of each other's attitudes and behavior. It should be noted that much of the groundwork can be broken by the use of discussion groups with the psychiatrist acting as a leader, with groups composed of masters or teachers, and in separate groups, the eleven- and twelve-year students. One of the greatest rewards is the students' sincere interest in such discussion groups. The numbers need not be limited. I have had as many as 100 and more in such groups, with excellent rapport between myself, as leader, and the students. The presence of the psychiatrist as an accepted member of the school family tends to make the masters and teachers more sensitive and alert to the significance of emotional problems and their recognition. As a result the teachers feel less threatened and more secure. They begin to think of the student as being emotionally upset rather than as "bad" or "lazy." It is frequently possible for the master or teacher to help an adolescent under the guidance of the psychiatrist, without the psychiatrist ever seeing the student involved. Frequently one sees that the problem in a particular student in some of the private schools might best be answered by removing the youngster from the school and sending him back to his home to live, with attendance at a school in his own community, either private or public, plus the use of psychiatric help, if indicated, in his home environment.

The types of problems seen are usually mild to moderate. Only occasionally does one see severe psychotic states. The majority of them rather fall into the group that strikes me as being best understood as behavior problems or academic failures. Certainly some 80 plus per cent of the youngsters seen fall into these latter categories. They do not require intensive or prolonged therapy. This attitude is emphasized by Drs. Josselyn, Peltz, and Berman. The school psychiatrist can do a great deal with visits that occur on only each third or fourth week end, during which he spends two or three days at the school. He can then see youngsters referred by the school physician or the masters, or by the students themselves. Many youngsters can be seen in the doctor's office during the summer, Christmas, and the spring holidays, without being seen during the times of school attendance, if such attendance is away from home. If, however, it appears that the interval is too long for the particular student, one can break up the period between holidays and have the patient come to the office from the school for one or two consecutive visits. Strenuous efforts should be made to see both parents. More than half the youngsters come from broken homes and, in such instances, seeing the stepparents can be of great help in clarifying the environmental circumstances in which the patient has to live. The school psychiatrist should make a point of familiarizing himself with school procedures, limitations, and requirements imposed on students in the particular school, as well as learning the traditions and major interests of the school as a whole.

The actual duration of the therapeutic session is variable. Some patients are bored to tears within the half hour, and others seem to become productive just at the half-hour point.

Time arrangement with the adolescent should therefore be flexible, allowing range of thirty to forty-five minutes.

In all instances, it is essential that the youngster be given to understand at the start of treatment that the material discussed in each session is confidential and will be so treated by the psychiatrist without discussion of it with masters, teachers, or parents. However, it is also clearly stated that each of these individuals will be given a diagnostic impression, with some clarification as to the possible duration of treatment. Rarely does one ask for exceptional treatment in terms of curriculum or school activities for any youngster who is under treatment. It is essential that students getting psychiatric help be treated exactly as the other students are in every respect. They should be made to feel that they do not differ from the other students just because they see the psychiatrist.

In Dr. Berman's chapter on clinic practice, one can see much of the same picture as one sees in private practice. The difference here seems to be that the degree of emotional disturbance is, on the average, greater than what one sees in private practice or in private and school practice. There are, however, enough youngsters who can and do respond to short-term therapy, and this is well pointed up by some of Dr. Berman's case reports.

Dr. Robinson, in his chapter on residential school plus inpatient treatment, makes two essential points which warrant emphasis. The first is the role that the parents play in the entire therapeutic situation. He has utilized parents in terms of direct therapy with them, and helps them use these new insights in their relationship with the child. Fundamentally, this approach is of major importance. It is obvious that the adolescent will ultimately have to re-establish a homeostatic relationship with his family for best resolution of whatever emotional problems are presented. The second important point which he makes is that disturbed adolescents who appear at first glance to be seriously or malignantly ill actually can and do respond to intensive therapy in a specialized milieu where the efforts of all the individuals involved in the care of these youngsters are directed toward understanding them and helping them to reach a resolution of those problems.

Drs. Harris and Heald, in their chapter on "Psychotherapy of Adolescents by Pediatrician and Psychiatrist at Combined Clinic and Inpatient Hospital Level," point up an important trend in medical graduate education which warrants wide dissemination. The early recognition, by pediatricians, of the part that emotional problems play in the behavior and organic syndromes of preadolescent and early adolescent youngsters as well as during the latency period is important as a preventive psychiatric program. It is bound to result in correction at an early enough level so that without too much or too intense therapy a great many of the problems can be dealt with. Another important aspect of their program has to do with the training of pediatricians by psychiatrists in how to deal with these emotional problems. This makes available a large additional group of therapists equipped to deal with emotional disease or illness in their early stages. Their approach and their results are reflected in their case reports.

Drs. Greaves and Regan give an excellent description of the approaches utilized in a hospital setting for the treatment of the more severely disturbed adolescents. Although these youngsters constitute a small percentage of the total seen on an outpatient level, they are a large enough group so that the problem of finding institutions or hospitals where they can receive adequate treatment is indeed a great one. One of our most serious problems in the treatment of mental illness is the paucity of referral sources for such treatment of adolescents. Many of the points that they make should be of value to groups who contemplate providing hospital care for seriously disturbed adolescents. The question of integration with adults on floors or wards of the hospital, as well as the problems in the hospital of the relations that develop between adolescents and adults, and with each other, is well outlined. Their report illustrates many of the problems with which they are faced.

Chapter 8 by Dr. Pottash was added because it provides an exact recording of what actually occurs in the therapeutic interview with an adolescent. Furthermore, the dynamic interpretation of the material presented, as well as the action in the interview, will give insight to the reader into the role that the psychiatrist plays in such a therapeutic relationship. We are indebted to Dr. M. Royden Astley, former training analyst with the Philadelphia Psychoanalytic Institute, for his help in these interpretations.

We added Mr. C. Thurston Chase's chapter on "Therapy of the Adolescent from a Schoolmaster's Standpoint" to present a layman but professional teacher's point of view in the handling of problems as they come to him in a boarding school. In his chapter he points out that youngsters with problems present themselves through the avenues of academic failure, behavioral difficulties, or by being withdrawn. He reviews his interviewing techniques and use of psychological testing procedures to evaluate the nature of the problem. Psychometric measurements give him an index as to intellectual capacity and the role it may play in the problem. Projective techniques in psychological testing give him some insights into the nature and extent of psychopathology present. In this regard, he utilizes expert clinical psychologists for interpretation of test results. Their recommendations may vary from a discussion of the findings with the parents as well as the masters, to guidance as regards improving the relationships between the child and his parents and teachers. The master or headmaster tries to implement the information gained in this way. They utilize guidance principles outlined to them in an attempt to improve the situation. If the problem is one that warrants the intervention of the psychiatrist, he is called in for consultation. The psychiatrist makes his decision as regards therapy of the youngsters, with or without change of school. An effort is made to keep the school program of these youngsters as much as possible on a par with that of their peers so that they do not stand out as being different from their contemporaries. In outlining his program, Mr. Chase uses case material to illustrate the various points in his program.

Probably one of the most difficult definitions to express is the one which describes the normal adolescent. I particularly admire the description by Dr. William Peltz, which in essence is as follows: "In the normal adolescent, one sees these deviations. Restlessness, confusion, and impatience. They show a lack of stability with fluctuating enthusiasms and intense infatuations. Laziness, forgetfulness, and inconsistency fit within the framework of adolescence. There is aggressive self-assertion with desire for independence on the one hand, and ever-present dependency on the other. They desire privileges but so frequently appear to lack a sense of obligation and responsibility. There are high ideals one moment and outrageous behavior the next. They frequently have feelings of isolation and of not being understood. They have truly colorful daydreams and fantasies, all of which belong to this developmental period."

BIBLIOGRAPHY

1. AICHHORN, AUGUST: *Wayward Youth.* New York: Viking Press, 1938.
2. ALEXANDER, FRANZ: *Psychoanalytic Therapy.* New York: Ronald Press, 1946.
3. APPEL, KENNETH E.: *Practical Examination of Personality and Behavior Disorders:* Adults and Children. New York: Macmillan, 1936.
4. BAWKIN, HARRY & BAWKIN, RUTH M.: *Clinical Management of Behavior Disorders in Children.* Philadelphia: Saunders, 1953.
5. BERMAN, S.: Psychotherapeutic Techniques with Adolescents. *Am. J. Orthopsychiat., 24*:238-245, 1954.
6. BETTELHEIM, BRUNO: *Love Is Not Enough.* Glencoe, Ill.: Free Press, 1950.
7. BLOS, PETER: *The Adolescent Personality.* New York: Appleton-Century-Croft, 1941.
8. —— Psychological Counseling of College Students. *Am. J. Orthopsychiat., 16,* 1946.
9. —— The Contribution of Psychoanalysis to the Treatment of Adolescents. In: *Psychoanalysis and Social Work,* ed. M. Heiman. New York: International Universities Press, 1953.
10. DEUTSCH, FELIX: *Applied Psychoanalysis.* New York: Grune & Stratton, 1949.
11. DEUTSCH, HELENE: *The Psychology of Women,* 2 Vols. New York: Grune & Stratton, 1944, 1945.
12. DIETHELM, OSKAR: *Treatment in Psychiatry.* Springfield: Thomas, 1955.
13. EISSLER, K. R.: Ego-Psychological Implications of the Psychoanalytic Treatment of Delinquents. *The Psychoanalytic Study of the Child,* 5:97-121. New York: International Universities Press, 1950.
14. ENGLISH, O. SPURGEON & PEARSON, GERALD H. J.: *Common Neurosis of Children and Adults.* New York: Norton, 1937.
15. ERIKSON, ERIK H.: *Childhood and Society.* New York: Norton, 1950.
16. —— The Problem of Ego Identity. *J. Am. Psychoanal. Assoc.,* 4:56-121, 1956.

17. FRAIBERG, SELMA: Some Considerations in the Introduction to Therapy in Puberty. *The Psychoanalytic Study of the Child, 10*:264-286. New York: International Universities Press, 1955.

18. FREUD, ANNA: *The Ego and the Mechanisms of Defense.* New York: International Universities Press, 1946.

19. FROMM-REICHMANN, FRIEDA: *Principles of Intensive Psychotherapy.* Chicago: University of Chicago Press, 1950.

20. GALLAGHER, ROSWELL: *Understanding Your Son's Adolescence.* Boston: Little, Brown, 1951.

21. GESELL, ARNOLD, ILG, FRANCES L., & AMES, LOUISE B.: *Youth: The Years from Ten to Sixteen.* New York: Harper, 1956.

22. GITELSON, MAXWELL: Direct Psychotherapy of Children. *Arch. Neurol. & Psychiat., 43*:1208, 1940.

23. —— Direct Psychotherapy in Adolescence. *Am. J. Orthopsychiat., 12*:1-25, 1942.

24. —— Character Synthesis: The Psychotherapeutic Problem of Adolescence. *Am. J. Orthopsychiat., 18*:422-431, 1948.

25. GROUP FOR THE ADVANCEMENT OF PSYCHIATRY: *The Role of Psychiatrists in Colleges and Universities.* Report No. 17, 1950.

26. HARTMANN, HEINZ, KRIS, ERNST, & LOEWENSTEIN, RUDOLPH M.: Comments on the Formation of Psychic Structure. *The Psychoanalytic Study of the Child, 2*:11-37. New York: International Universities Press, 1946.

27. HEELY, ALLAN, V.: *Why the Private School?* New York: Harper, 1951.

28. HUGHES, J. G.: A Practical Approach to Common Behavior Problems. *Ped. Clin. N. Am.,* 447-466, May 1954.

29. JOHNSON, ADELAIDE M.: Sanctions for Superego Lacunae of Adolescents. In: *Searchlights on Delinquency,* ed. K. R. Eissler. New York: International Universities Press, 1949.

30. —— & FISHBACK, DORA: Analysis of a Disturbed Adolescent Girl and Collaborative Psychiatric Treatment of the Mother. *Am. J. Orthopsychiat., 14*:195-203, 1944.

31. —— & SZUREK, S., FALSTEIN, E.: Collaborative Psychiatric Treatment in Parent-Child Problems. *Am. J. Orthopsychiat., 12,* 1942.

32. JOSSELYN, IRENE M.: *The Adolescent and His World.* New York: Family Service Association of America, 1952.

33. —— The Ego in Adolescence. *Am. J. Orthopsychiat., 24*:233-237, 1954.

34. KANNER, LEO: *Child Psychiatry.* Springfield: Thomas, 1955.

35. KINSEY, A.: *Sexual Behavior of the Human Male.* Philadelphia: Saunders, 1951.

36. —— *Sexual Behavior of the Human Female.* Philadelphia: Saunders, 1953.

37. KLEIN, MELANIE: *The Psycho-Analysis of Children.* London: Hogarth Press, 1946.

38. LANDER, JOSEPH: The Pubertal Struggle Against the Instincts. *Am. J. Orthopsychiat., 12,* 1942.

39. LEVINE, MAURICE: Principles of Psychiatric Treatment. In: *Dynamic Psychiatry,* ed. F. Alexander & H. Ross. Chicago: University of Chicago Press, 1952.

40. NATIONAL COUNCIL OF INDEPENDENT SCHOOLS: Individual Attention—Myth or Reality. April 1956.

41. PEARSON, GERALD H. J.: *Emotional Disorders of Children.* New York: Norton, 1954.

42. —— *Psychoanalysis and the Education of the Child.* New York: Norton, 1954.

43. REDL, FRITZ & WINEMAN, DAVID: *Children Who Hate.* Glencoe, Ill.: Free Press, 1951.

44. —— *Controls from Within.* Glencoe, Ill.: Free Press, 1952.

45. RUBE, PIERRE: The Inner World of Adolescence. *Am. J. Psychother., 9:*673-691, 1954.

46. SADLER, WILLIAM S.: *A Doctor Talks to Teen-Agers.* St. Louis: Mosby, 1948.

47. SARGENT, PORTER E.: *The Handbook of Private Schools.* Boston (11 Beacon Street), 37th ed., 1956.

48. SCHMIDEBERG, MELITTA: The Psychoanalysis of Asocial Children and Adolescents. *Int. J. Psychoanal., 16:*22-48, 1935.

49. SCHULMAN, IRVING: The Dynamics of Certain Reactions to Group Psychotherapy. *Int. J. Group Psychother., 2:*334-343, 1952.

50. SLAVSON, S. R.: *Analytic Group Psychotherapy with Children, Adolescents and Adults.* New York: Columbia University Press, 1950.

51. SPIEGEL, LEO A.: A Review of Contributions to a Psychoanalytic Theory of Adolescence: Individual Aspects. *The Psychoanalytic Study of the Child, 6:*375-394. New York: International Universities Press, 1951.

52. STOLZ, R. & STOLZ, L. M.: *Somatic Development of Adolescent Boys.* New York: Macmillan, 1951.

53. STUART, H. C.: Normal Growth and Development during Adolescence. *New Engl. J. Med.,* May 1946.

54. SULLIVAN, H. S.: *The Psychiatric Interview.* New York: Norton, 1954.

55. Symposium: Difficulties of Adolescence in the Boy. *Nerv. Child, 4* (No. 1), 1944-45.

56. Symposium: Difficulties of Adolescence in the Girl. *Nerv. Child, 4* (No. 2), 1944-45.

57. SZUREK, S. A.: Some Impressions from Clinical Experience with

Delinquents. In: *Searchlights on Delinquency,* ed. K. R. Eissler. New York: International Universities Press, 1949.

58. WECHSLER, DAVID: *The Measurement of Adult Intelligence.* Baltimore: Williams & Wilkins, 1944.

59. WITTELS, FRITZ: The Ego of the Adolescent. In: *Searchlights on Delinquency,* ed. K. R. Eissler. New York: International Universities Press, 1949.

60. WOLBERG, LEWIS R.: *The Technique of Psychotherapy.* New York: Grune & Stratton, 1954.

61. ZISKIND, E.: Training in Psychotherapy for All Physicians. *J. Am. Med. Assoc., 147:*1223-1225, 1951.

INDEX